Complicated Kris Northern

"This image illustrates some of the best qualities of fractals—infinity, reiteration, and self similarity."– **Kris Northern**

D1365056

Investigations
IN NUMBER, DATA, AND SPACE®

Photographs

Every effort has been made to secure permission and provide appropriate credit for photographic material. The publisher deeply regrets any omission and pledges to correct errors called to its attention in subsequent editions.

Unless otherwise acknowledged, all photographs are the property of Scott Foresman, a division of Pearson Education.

Photo locators denoted as follows: Top (T), Center (C), Bottom (B), Left (L), Right (R), Background (Bkgd).

23 SuperStock; 78 SuperStock

Glenview, Illinois • Boston, Massachusetts
Chandler, Arizona • Upper Saddle River, New Jersey

T E R C

The Investigations curriculum was developed by TERC, Cambridge, MA.

This material is based on work supported by the National Science Foundation ("NSF") under Grant No. ESI-0095450. Any opinions, findings, and conclusions or recommendations expressed in this material are those of the author(s) and do not necessarily reflect the views of the National Science Foundation.

ISBN-13: 978-0-328-60017-5

ISBN-10: 0-328-60017-2

2 3 4 5 6 7 8 9 10 V003 14 13 12 11

T E R C

Co-Principal Investigators

Susan Jo Russell

Karen Economopoulos

Authors

Lucy Wittenberg
Director Grades 3–5

Karen Economopoulos
Director Grades K–2

Virginia Bastable
(SummerMath for Teachers, Mt. Holyoke College)

Katie Hickey Bloomfield

Keith Cochran

Darrell Earnest

Arusha Hollister

Nancy Horowitz

Erin Leidl

Megan Murray

Young Oh

Beth W. Perry

Susan Jo Russell

Deborah Schifter
(Education Development Center)

Kathy Sillman

Administrative Staff

Amy Taber
Project Manager

Beth Bergeron

Lorraine Brooks

Emi Fujiwara

Contributing Authors

Denise Baumann

Jennifer DiBrienza

Hollee Freeman

Paula Hooper

Jan Mokros

Stephen Monk
(University of Washington)

Mary Beth O'Connor

Judy Storeygard

Cornelia Tierney

Elizabeth Van Cleef

Carol Wright

Technology

Jim Hammerman

Classroom Field Work

Amy Appell

Rachel E. Davis

Traci Higgins

Julia Thompson

Collaborating Teachers

This group of dedicated teachers carried out extensive field testing in their classrooms, met regularly to discuss issues of teaching and learning mathematics, provided feedback to staff, welcomed staff into their classrooms to document students' work, and contributed both suggestions and written material that has been incorporated into the curriculum.

Bethany Altchek

Linda Amaral

Kimberly Beauregard

Barbara Bernard

Nancy Buell

Rose Christiansen

Chris Colbath-Hess

Lisette Colon

Kim Cook

Frances Cooper

Kathleen Drew

Rebeka Eston Salemi

Thomas Fisher

Michael Flynn

Holly Ghazey

Susan Gillis

Danielle Harrington

Elaine Herzog

Francine Hiller

Kirsten Lee Howard

Liliana Klass

Leslie Kramer

Melissa Lee Andrichak

Kelley Lee Sadowski

Jennifer Levitan

Mary Lou LoVecchio

Kristen McEnaney

Maura McGrail

Kathe Millett

Florence Molyneaux

Amy Monkiewicz

Elizabeth Monopoli

Carol Murray

Robyn Musser

Christine Norrman

Deborah O'Brien

Timothy O'Connor

Anne Marie O'Reilly

Mark Paige

Margaret Riddle

Karen Schweitzer

Elisabeth Seyferth

Susan Smith

Debra Sorvillo

Shoshanah Starr

Janice Szymaszek

Karen Tobin

JoAnn Trauschke

Ana Vaisenstein

Yvonne Watson

Michelle Woods

Mary Wright

Note: Unless otherwise noted, all contributors listed above were staff of the Education Research Collaborative at TERC during their work on the curriculum. Other affiliations during the time of development are listed.

Advisors

Deborah Lowenberg Ball,
University of Michigan

Hyman Bass, Professor of Mathematics and Mathematics Education
University of Michigan

Mary Canner, Principal, Natick Public Schools

Thomas Carpenter, Professor of Curriculum and Instruction,
University of Wisconsin-Madison

Janis Freckmann, Elementary Mathematics Coordinator,
Milwaukee Public Schools

Lynne Godfrey, Mathematics Coach,
Cambridge Public Schools

Ginger Hanlon, Instructional Specialist in Mathematics,
New York City Public Schools

DeAnn Huinker, Director, Center for Mathematics and
Science Education Research, University of Wisconsin-Milwaukee

James Kaput, Professor of Mathematics, University of
Massachusetts-Dartmouth

Kate Kline, Associate Professor, Department of Mathematics
and Statistics, Western Michigan University

Jim Lewis, Professor of Mathematics,
University of Nebraska-Lincoln

William McCallum, Professor of Mathematics,
University of Arizona

Harriet Pollatsek, Professor of Mathematics,
Mount Holyoke College

Debra Shein-Gerson, Elementary Mathematics Specialist,
Weston Public Schools

Gary Shevell, Assistant Principal,
New York City Public Schools

Liz Sweeney, Elementary Math Department,
Boston Public Schools

Lucy West, Consultant, Metamorphosis:
Teaching Learning Communities, Inc.

This revision of the curriculum was built on the work of the many
authors who contributed to the first edition (published between
1994 and 1998). We acknowledge the critical contributions of
these authors in developing the content and pedagogy of
Investigations:

Authors

Joan Akers

Michael T. Battista

Douglas H. Clements

Karen Economopoulos

Marlene Kliman

Jan Mokros

Megan Murray

Ricardo Nemirovsky

Andee Rubin

Susan Jo Russell

Cornelia Tierney

Contributing Authors

Mary Berle-Carman

Rebecca B. Corwin

Rebeka Eston

Claryce Evans

Anne Goodrow

Cliff Konold

Chris Mainhart

Sue McMillen

Jerrie Moffet

Tracy Noble

Kim O'Neil

Mark Ogonowski

Julie Sarama

Amy Shulman Weinberg

Margie Singer

Virginia Woolley

Tracey Wright

Contents

UNIT 7

Parts of a Whole, Parts of a Group

Investigations

CURRICULUM

Overview of Program Components

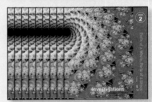

The **Curriculum Units** are the teaching guides. (See far right.)

Implementing Investigations in Grade 2 offers suggestions for implementing the curriculum. It also contains a comprehensive index.

The **Differentiation and Intervention Guide** offers additional activities for each Investigation to support the range of learners.

Investigations for the Interactive Whiteboard provides whole-class instructional support to enhance each session.

The **Resource Masters and Transparencies CD** contains all reproducible materials that support instruction. The **Shapes CD** provides an environment in which students investigate a variety of geometric ideas.

FOR STUDENTS

The **Student Activity Book** contains the consumable student pages (Recording Sheets, Homework, Practice, and so on).

The **Student Math Handbook** contains Math Words and Ideas pages and Games directions.

The *Investigations* Curriculum

Investigations in Number, Data, and Space® is a K–5 mathematics curriculum designed to engage students in making sense of mathematical ideas. Six major goals guided the development of the *Investigations in Number, Data, and Space®* curriculum. The curriculum is designed to:

- Support students to make sense of mathematics and learn that they can be mathematical thinkers

- Focus on computational fluency with whole numbers as a major goal of the elementary grades

- Provide substantive work in important areas of mathematics—rational numbers, geometry, measurement, data, and early algebra—and connections among them

- Emphasize reasoning about mathematical ideas

- Communicate mathematics content and pedagogy to teachers

- Engage the range of learners in understanding mathematics

Underlying these goals are three guiding principles that are touchstones for the *Investigations* team as we approach both students and teachers as agents of their own learning:

1. *Students have mathematical ideas.* Students come to school with ideas about numbers, shapes, measurements, patterns, and data. If given the opportunity to learn in an environment that stresses making sense of mathematics, students build on the ideas they already have and learn about new mathematics they have never encountered. Students learn that they are capable of having mathematical ideas, applying what they know to new situations, and thinking and reasoning about unfamiliar problems.

2. *Teachers are engaged in ongoing learning* about mathematics content, pedagogy, and student learning. The curriculum provides material for professional development, to be used by teachers individually or in groups, that supports teachers' continued learning as they use the curriculum over several years. The *Investigations* curriculum materials are designed as much to be a dialogue with teachers as to be a core of content for students.

3. *Teachers collaborate with the students and curriculum materials* to create the curriculum as enacted in the classroom. The only way for a good curriculum to be used well is for teachers to be active participants in implementing it. Teachers use the curriculum to maintain a clear, focused, and coherent agenda for mathematics teaching. At the same time, they observe and listen carefully to students, try to understand how they are thinking, and make teaching decisions based on these observations.

Investigations is based on experience from research and practice, including field testing that involved documentation of thousands of hours in classrooms, observations of students, input from teachers, and analysis of student work. As a result, the curriculum addresses the learning needs of real students in a wide range of classrooms and communities. The investigations are carefully designed to invite all students into mathematics—girls and boys; members of diverse cultural, ethnic, and language groups; and students with a wide variety of strengths, needs, and interests.

Based on this extensive classroom testing, the curriculum takes seriously the time students need to develop a strong conceptual foundation and skills based on that foundation. Each curriculum unit focuses on an area of content in depth, providing time for students to develop and practice ideas across a variety of activities and contexts that build on each other. Daily guidelines for time spent on class sessions, Classroom Routines (K–3), and Ten-Minute Math (3–5) reflect the commitment to devoting adequate time to mathematics in each school day.

About This Curriculum Unit

This **Curriculum Unit** is one of nine teaching guides in Grade 2. The seventh unit in Grade 2 is *Parts of a Whole, Parts of a Group.*

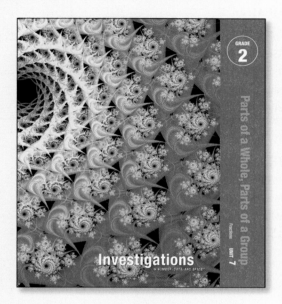

- The **Introduction and Overview** section organizes and presents the instructional materials, provides background information, and highlights important features specific to this unit.

- Each Curriculum Unit contains several **Investigations.** Each Investigation focuses on a set of related mathematical ideas.

- Investigations are divided into one-hour **Sessions,** or lessons.

- Sessions have a combination of these parts: **Activity, Discussion, Math Workshop, Assessment Activity,** and **Session Follow-Up.**

- Each session also has one or more **Classroom Routines** that are done outside of math time.

- At the back of the book is a collection of **Teacher Notes** and **Dialogue Boxes** that provide professional development related to the unit.

- Also included at the back of the book are the **Student Math Handbook** pages for this unit.

- The **Index** provides a way to look up important words or terms.

Overview

O F   T H I S   U N I T

Investigation	Session	Day	
INVESTIGATION 1 **One Half** Students begin their study of fractions by focusing on fractions as equal parts of a whole. They use their existing knowledge of one half as they find one half of a single object and one half of a set of objects.	**1.1** What Is a Half?	1	
	1.2 Halves of Blocks and Balloon Bunches	2	
	1.3 Halves of Blocks, Balloons, and Rectangles	3	
	1.4 Halves of Rectangles and Sharing a Picnic Workshop	4	
INVESTIGATION 2 **Halves, Thirds, and Fourths** Students divide objects and groups into more than two equal parts and name quantities that contain more than one equal part. As they make Fraction Flags and solve Sharing Stories, students work with unit fractions $(\frac{1}{2}, \frac{1}{3}, \frac{1}{4})$ and fractions with numerators greater than one $(\frac{2}{3}, \frac{3}{4})$.	**2.1** Fourths of a Square	5	
	2.2 Thirds of a Flag	6	
	2.3 More Fraction Flags	7	
	2.4 Fraction Flag Posters	8	
	2.5 Sharing Among Friends	9	
	2.6 End-of-Unit Assessment	10	

Each *Investigations* session has some combination of these five parts: **Activity, Discussion, Math Workshop, Assessment Activity,** and **Session Follow-Up.** These session parts are indicated in the chart below. Each session also has one **Classroom Routine** that is done outside of math time.

 Ⓦ Interactive Whiteboard

Classroom Routines

Activity	Discussion	Math Workshop	Assessment Activity	Session Follow-Up
Ⓦ	Ⓦ			●
Ⓦ		●	●	●
Ⓦ	Ⓦ	●		●
●	Ⓦ	●		●
Ⓦ●	Ⓦ			●
Ⓦ●				●
●	Ⓦ			●
●	●			●
●	Ⓦ			●
	Ⓦ		Ⓦ	●

Quick Images	Today's Number	What Time Is It?	How Many Pockets?
Ⓦ			
	Ⓦ		
		Ⓦ	
			Ⓦ
Ⓦ			
	Ⓦ		
		Ⓦ	
Ⓦ			
	Ⓦ		
		Ⓦ	

Mathematics

IN THIS UNIT

Parts of a Whole, Parts of a Group is the Grade 2 unit in the rational numbers strand of *Investigations*. These units develop ideas about understanding, representing, and computing with fractions and decimal fractions.

LOOKING BACK Even before they are taught these ideas in school, many children encounter fractions through situations in which they share. Perhaps they have a set of cards that they must distribute equally among those playing a game. The work of this unit builds on such informal experiences students are likely to have had with fractions.

Although this Grade 2 unit is the first unit in the rational numbers strand, first-grade students encountered work with fractions in the unit *Fish Lengths and Animal Jumps* as they measured lengths that fell between whole numbers of units.

This unit focuses on the following 3 Mathematical Emphases:

1 Rational Numbers Understanding fractions as equal parts of a whole

Math Focus Points

◆ Finding equal parts of a whole and naming them with fractions (e.g., $\frac{1}{2}$ is one of two equal parts; $\frac{1}{3}$ is one of three equal parts, and so on)

◆ Showing one half of an object

◆ Determining whether a block is half of another block

◆ Determining whether a region is half of a given rectangle

◆ Seeing different ways to make fourths of a square

◆ Recognizing the equivalence of different fourths of the same object

◆ Identifying halves, thirds, and fourths of regions

◆ Identifying and naming fractional parts that have numerators greater than 1 (e.g., $\frac{2}{3}, \frac{2}{4}, \frac{3}{4}$)

Although students may know that fractions involve dividing objects into parts, they may not understand that those parts must be equal and must use up all the material. Thus, one half is one of two equal parts, and the two parts together make up one whole.

In this unit, students learn that fractions are used to represent equal parts of whole objects such as a rectangle, a sandwich, or a ball of clay. Students work with unit fractions ($\frac{1}{2}, \frac{1}{3}, \frac{1}{4}$), which represent one part of a whole, and they work with fractions such as $\frac{2}{3}, \frac{2}{4}$, and $\frac{3}{4}$ that represent more than one part of a whole. For example, when looking at a rectangle that is divided into four equal parts—three of which are shaded orange—students learn that three fourths comprises three of four equal parts.

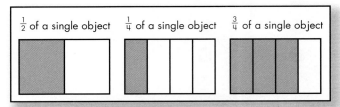

2 Rational Numbers Understanding fractions as equal parts of a group

Math Focus Points

◆ Finding equal parts of a group and naming them with fractions (e.g., $\frac{1}{2}$ is one of two equal parts; $\frac{1}{3}$ is one of three equal parts, and so on)

◆ Finding one half of a set

◆ Solving problems about finding halves of quantities in different contexts

◆ Solving problems that result in mixed numbers

◆ Finding thirds and fourths of sets

◆ Finding fractions of sets

Fractions can also be thought of in terms of parts of sets. For example, one might talk about one half of a bunch of 12 balloons or one third of a jar of 15 pennies. In this unit, students work with $\frac{1}{2}, \frac{1}{3}$, and $\frac{1}{4}$ of sets.

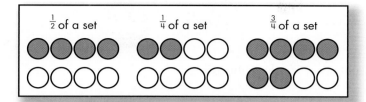

$\frac{1}{2}$ of a set $\frac{1}{4}$ of a set $\frac{3}{4}$ of a set

3 Rational Numbers **Using terms and notation**

Math Focus Points

- Learning the term *one half* and the notation $\frac{1}{2}$
- Learning the terms and notation for mixed numbers (e.g., *one and a half* and $1\frac{1}{2}$)
- Learning the term *one fourth* and the notation $\frac{1}{4}$
- Learning the term *one third* and the notation $\frac{1}{3}$
- Learning the terms and notation for fractions that contain more than one part (e.g., $\frac{2}{3}$, $\frac{2}{4}$, and $\frac{3}{4}$)

In this unit, students learn how fractions are expressed in words (one half, two thirds) and represented with numbers ($\frac{1}{2}$, $\frac{2}{3}$). Students use fractions in different contexts including folding paper squares, coloring rectangular Fraction Flags, and sharing sets of objects among different numbers of people. Students come to understand that in fraction notation, the bottom number, or denominator, represents the number of equal parts in the whole.

In the example of this Fraction Flag, the flag is divided into four equal parts (denominator). When representing the fraction of the rectangle that is shaded, the top number, 3 (numerator), designates the number of those parts that are shaded.

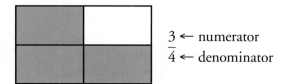

$\dfrac{3 \leftarrow \text{numerator}}{4 \leftarrow \text{denominator}}$

Students also learn the notation for mixed numbers through dividing sets. For example, if two girls share three sandwiches, each girl gets $1\frac{1}{2}$ sandwiches.

Classroom Routines focus on

- Developing and analyzing visual images for quantities
- Combining groups of tens and ones
- Generating equivalent expressions for a number
- Developing fluency with addition and subtraction
- Using standard notation ($+$, $-$, $=$) to record expressions and write equations
- Using clocks as tools for keeping track of and measuring time
- Naming, notating, and telling time to the hour, half hour, and quarter hour on digital and analog clocks
- Determining the number of minutes in hours, half hours, and quarter hours
- Counting by 5s
- Making predictions about data
- Collecting, counting, representing, discussing, interpreting, and comparing data
- Using known combinations (i.e. combinations that make 10) to combine numbers
- Developing strategies for solving addition problems with many addends

LOOKING FORWARD Ideas about fractions will arise again in the Grade 2 measurement unit, *Measuring Length and Time.* When measuring the length of an object, students will consider how to represent partial units. In the fourth investigation of the unit, while studying timelines, students will work with half-hour and quarter-hour intervals.

In Grade 3, students deepen their understanding of the fraction work they began in Grade 2 as they continue to work on the meaning of fractions as equal parts of a whole object, area, or group. They will compare commonly used fractions, find fraction equivalents, work with decimal fractions (e.g., 0.5, 0.25), and begin to add fractions.

Assessment

IN THIS UNIT

ONGOING ASSESSMENT: Observing Students at Work

The following sessions provide **Ongoing Assessment: Observing Students at Work** opportunities:

- **Session 1.1, p. 22**
- **Session 1.2, pp. 28 and 29**
- **Session 1.3, p. 33**

- **Session 1.4, p. 38**
- **Session 2.1, pp. 50 and 51**
- **Session 2.2, p. 56**

- **Session 2.3, p. 63**
- **Session 2.4, p. 65**
- **Session 2.5, p. 71**

WRITING OPPORTUNITIES

The following sessions have **writing** opportunities for students to explain their mathematical thinking:

- **Session 1.3, p. 35**
  Student Activity Book, p. 16

- **Session 1.4, p. 40**
  Student Activity Book, p. 19

- **Session 2.5, pp. 71–72**
  Student Activity Book, pp. 33–35

PORTFOLIO OPPORTUNITIES

The following sessions have work appropriate for a **portfolio:**

- **Session 1.1, pp. 21–22**
  Student Activity Book, pp. 1–5

- **Session 1.4, p. 38**
  Student Activity Book, pp. 17–18

- **Session 2.3, pp. 61–62**
  Student Activity Book, pp. 27–30

- **Session 2.5, pp. 71–72**
  Student Activity Book, pp. 33–35

- **Session 2.6, pp. 74–75**
  M24–M25, End-of-Unit Assessment

Assessing the Benchmarks

Observing students as they engage in conversation about their ideas is a primary means to assess their mathematical understanding. Consider all of your students' work, not just the written assessments. See the chart below for suggestions about key activities to observe.

See the **Differentiation and Intervention Guide** for quizzes that can be used after each Investigation.

Benchmarks in This Unit	Key Activities to Observe	Assessment
1. Identify $\frac{1}{2}$, $\frac{1}{3}$, and $\frac{1}{4}$ of a region.	**Session 1.1:** What Is a Half? **Session 1.3:** Halves/Not Halves of Rectangles **Session 2.1:** Folding and Folding Again **Session 2.2:** Fraction Flags	**Session 2.6 End-of-Unit Assessment:** Problem 1 **Session 1.2–1.4 Assessment:** Fractions as Equal Parts ☑
2. Find $\frac{1}{2}$ of a set of objects.	**Session 1.2:** Bunches of Balloons **Session 1.2:** Sharing Pennies **Session 1.4:** Going on a Picnic	**Session 2.6 End-of-Unit Assessment:** Problem 2 **Session 1.2–1.4 Assessment:** Fractions as Equal Parts ☑
3. Recognize that a fraction divides the whole into equal parts.	**Session 1.1:** What Is a Half? **Session 1.3:** Halves/Not Halves of Rectangles **Session 2.1:** Folding and Folding Again **Session 2.2:** Fraction Flags	**Session 2.6 End-of-Unit Assessment:** Problem 3

 Checklist Available

Relating the Mathematical Emphases to the Benchmarks

Mathematical Emphases	Benchmarks
Rational Numbers Understanding fractions as equal parts of a whole	1, 3
Rational Numbers Understanding fractions as equal parts of a group	2, 3
Rational Numbers Using terms and notations	1, 2

Classroom Routines

Classroom Routines offer practice and review of key concepts for this grade level. These daily activities, to be done in ten minutes outside of math class, occur in a regular rotation every 4–5 days. Specific directions for the day's routine are provided in each session. For the full description and variations of each classroom routine see *Implementing Investigations in Grade 2*.

Quick Images

Students combine groups of tens and ones to determine the total number of squares in a given array and use standard notation to write equations that represent these amounts.

Math Focus Points

◆ Developing and analyzing visual images for quantities

◆ Combining groups of tens and ones

◆ Using standard notation ($+$, $-$, $=$) to write equations

Today's Number

Students generate combinations that use multiples of 5 and 10 and subtraction. They also solve problems about Today's Number in which different parts are missing. (For example, $20 - \underline{\quad} = 15$ and $\underline{\quad} - 25 = 15$.)

Math Focus Points

◆ Generating equivalent expressions for a number

◆ Developing fluency with addition and subtraction

◆ Using standard notation ($+$, $-$, $=$) to record expressions and write equations

What Time Is It?

Students determine the number of minutes in a quarter hour and discuss why 15 and 45 minutes are one quarter and three quarters of an hour. They also continue to practice telling and notating time to the hour, half hour, and quarter hour.

Math Focus Points

◆ Using clocks as tools for keeping track of and measuring time

◆ Naming, notating, and telling time to the hour, half hour, and quarter hour on digital and analog clocks

◆ Determining the number of minutes in hours, half hours, and quarter hours

◆ Counting by 5s

How Many Pockets?

Students work individually to record the class's pocket data on a class list and determine the total number of pockets the class has.

Math Focus Points

◆ Making predictions about data

◆ Collecting, counting, representing, discussing, interpreting, and comparing data

◆ Using known combinations (i.e. combinations that make 10) to combine numbers

◆ Developing strategies for solving addition problems with many addends

Practice and Review

Practice and review play a critical role in the *Investigations* program. The following components and features are available to provide regular reinforcement of key mathematical concepts and procedures.

Books	Features	In This Unit ...
Curriculum Unit	**Classroom Routines** offer practice and review of key concepts for this grade level. These daily activities, to be done in ten minutes outside of math class, occur in a regular rotation every 4–5 days. Specific directions for the day's routine are provided in each session. For the full description and variations of each classroom routine see *Implementing Investigations in Grade 2*.	• **All sessions**
Student Activity Book	**Daily Practice** pages in the *Student Activity Book* provide one of three types of written practice: **reinforcement** of the content of the unit, **ongoing review,** or **enrichment** opportunities. Some Daily Practice pages will also have Ongoing Review items with multiple-choice problems similar to those on standardized tests.	• **All sessions**
	Homework pages in the *Student Activity Book* are an extension of the work done in class. At times they help students prepare for upcoming activities.	• **Session 1.4** • **Session 2.3**
Student Math Handbook	**Math Words and Ideas** in the *Student Math Handbook* are pages that summarize key words and ideas. Most Words and Ideas pages have at least one exercise.	• **Student Math Handbook, pp. 84–92**
	Games pages are found in a section of the *Student Math Handbook*.	• **No games are introduced in this unit.**

Differentiation

Supporting the Range of Learners

The **Differentiation and Intervention Guide** provides Intervention, Extension, and Practice activities for use within each Investigation.

Sessions	1.1	1.2	1.3	1.4	2.1	2.2	2.3	2.4	2.5
Intervention	●	●		●	●		●	●	●
Extension		●	●	●		●		●	●
ELL	●	●		●	●	●			●

Intervention

Suggestions are made to support and engage students who are having difficulty with a particular idea, activity, or problem.

Extension

Suggestions are made to support and engage students who finish early or may be ready for additional challenge.

English Language Learners (ELL)

In this unit, students learn how to recognize, read, and write fractions. By the end of the unit, they must demonstrate comprehension of the portions represented by several fractions.

English Language Learners may be unfamiliar with vocabulary, such as *whole, half, equal,* and *pieces* used to explain the concept of fractions. Give English Language Learners time to practice and recognize these words before explaining the concept to the class. One way to do this is to provide a warm-up activity in which the whole class brainstorms personal connections they have with the content. While they work, review words with English Language Learners. Then allow them to listen to the connections the class generated.

To help students remember vocabulary and link terms to the proper fraction, post a visual and refer to it as new

concepts are introduced and reviewed. On the visual, write the numerical fractions and their expressions in English, and sketch a visual example beneath each. The first row of the chart may contain numerical fractions $\frac{1}{2}, \frac{1}{3}, \frac{1}{4}$, and $\frac{3}{4}$. The next row should contain their expressions in English (*one half, one third, one fourth,* and *three fourths*). The last row should contain each fraction illustrated by a rectangle divided into even parts. The rectangle under the column labeled $\frac{1}{2}$ should have one of two parts shaded. The one under $\frac{1}{3}$ should have one of three parts shaded, and so on. Explain the chart fraction by fraction. Say, **This is the fraction $\frac{1}{2}$. Here it is written in words. Here is a picture of $\frac{1}{2}$.** As you introduce new concepts, point to parts of the chart that apply.

Working with the Range of Learners is a set of episodes written by teachers that focuses on meeting the needs of the range of learners in the classroom. In the first section, *Setting up the Mathematical Community,* teachers write about how they create a supportive and productive learning environment in their classrooms. In the next section, *Accommodations for Learning,* teachers focus on specific modifications they make to meet the needs of some of their learners. In the last section, *Language and Representation,* teachers share how they help students use representations and develop language to investigate and express mathematical ideas. The questions at the end of each case provide a starting point for your own reflection or for discussion with colleagues. See *Implementing Investigations in Grade 2* for this set of episodes.

Mathematical Emphases

Rational Numbers Understanding fractions as equal parts of a whole

Math Focus Points

◆ Finding equal parts of a whole and naming them with fractions (e.g., $\frac{1}{2}$ is one of two equal parts; $\frac{1}{3}$ is one of three equal parts, and so on)

◆ Showing one half of an object

◆ Determining whether a block is half of another block

◆ Determining whether a region is half of a given rectangle

Rational Numbers Understanding fractions as equal parts of a group

Math Focus Points

◆ Finding equal parts of a group and naming them with fractions (e.g., $\frac{1}{2}$ is one of two equal parts; $\frac{1}{3}$ is one of three equal parts, and so on)

◆ Finding one half of a set

◆ Solving problems about finding halves of quantities in different contexts

◆ Solving problems that result in mixed numbers

Rational Numbers Using Terms and Notation

Math Focus Points

◆ Learning the term *one half* and the notation $\frac{1}{2}$

◆ Learning the terms and notation for mixed numbers (e.g., *one and a half* and $1\frac{1}{2}$)

One Half

SESSION 1.1 p. 20	Student Activity Book	Student Math Handbook	Professional Development: Read Ahead of Time	
What Is a Half? The session begins with a discussion of what *one half* means. Students work on story problems that involve dividing both single objects and sets in half. They share their solutions and discuss how the problems are similar.	1–6	84, 85, 86	• **Mathematics in This Unit,** p. 10 • **Teacher Note:** Learning About Fractions, p. 77 • **Dialogue Box:** What Is One Half?, p. 83	
SESSION 1.2 p. 25				
Halves of Blocks and Balloon Bunches Students are introduced to two activities about finding halves—halves of objects (Geoblocks) and halves of sets (bunches of balloons)—which they work on in Math Workshop.	7–13	86		
SESSION 1.3 p. 31				
Halves of Blocks, Balloons, and Rectangles An additional Math Workshop activity involves determining whether particular shapes are half or not half of a given rectangle. Students discuss finding halves of sets (bunches of balloons).	7–12, 14–16	86		
SESSION 1.4 p. 36				
Halves of Rectangles and Sharing a Picnic Workshop Students discuss finding halves of sets in which the objects can be divided into two equal parts. In Math Workshop, they find halves of sets that result in mixed numbers and continue determining which shapes are half of a rectangle. Students discuss which shapes make half of a rectangle and why.	14–15, 17–20	84, 85, 86, 92		

Classroom Routines See page 14 for an overview.

How Many Pockets?	Today's Number
• Class list (1 per student)	• Class number line
Quick Images	**What Time Is It?**
• T69, *Quick Images 1: Tens and Ones*	• M7, The Clock Make copies. (1 per student)
Cut apart the images.	• Student clocks (1 per pair)

Materials to Gather	Materials to Prepare
• **Crayons** (as needed) • **Color tiles** (optional)	• **M1–M2, Family Letter** Make copies. (1 per student) • **Chart paper** Label the chart paper "What We Know About $\frac{1}{2}$."
• **Geoblocks** (1 set per 6 students) • **Connecting cubes** (optional) • **Paper** (optional)	• **M4, Assessment checklist: Fractions as Equal Parts** Make copies (as needed) ✓
• **T70–T71 Halves and Not Halves of Rectangles** • **Container** • **Geoblocks** (1 set per 6 students) • **Connecting cubes** (optional) • **Paper** (optional) • **Crayons** (as needed)	• **M10, Pieces of Rectangles: Shapes A–F** Make 6 copies on cardstock. Cut apart the pieces, making 6 sets. If possible, laminate pieces and place them in a container. • **M5–M6, Family Letter** Make copies. (1 per student) • **Chart paper** Label the chart paper "Halves and Not Halves of Rectangles." Draw a rectangle on the chart that is 4 cm x 8 cm—exactly two times the size of Piece A on Pieces of Rectangles: Shapes A–F (M10). • **Chart paper** Create a three-column chart titled "Halves of Bunches." Label the second column "Split in Half?" and label the last column "How Many Does Each Girl Get?" In the first column "Number of Balloons," starting in the second row, include the following numbers, one number per row: 7, 8, 14, 11, 20. See page 34.

• **T70–T71 Halves and Not Halves of Rectangles**
  (from Session 1.3)
• **M10, Pieces of Rectangles: Shapes A–F** (from Session 1.3)
• **Chart: "Halves and Not Halves of Rectangles"**
  (from Session 1.3)
• **Crayons** (as needed)
• **Connecting cubes** (optional)
• **Paper** (optional)	

Overhead Transparency   ✓ Checklist Available

What Is a Half?

Math Focus Points

◆ Learning the term *one half* and the notation $\frac{1}{2}$

◆ Finding equal parts of a whole or a group and naming them with fractions (e.g., $\frac{1}{2}$ is one of two equal parts; $\frac{1}{3}$ is one of three equal parts, and so on)

◆ Finding one half of a set

◆ Showing one half of an object

Vocabulary
one half
fraction
equal
half

Today's Plan		Materials
1 ACTIVITY **What Is a Half?**	35 MIN PAIRS CLASS	• *Student Activity Book,* pp. 1–5 • Chart: "What We Know About $\frac{1}{2}$"* • Crayons; color tiles
2 DISCUSSION **Half of Objects/Half of Sets**	25 MIN CLASS	• *Student Activity Book,* pp. 1–5 (from Activity 1)
3 SESSION FOLLOW-UP **Daily Practice**		• *Student Activity Book,* p. 6 • *Student Math Handbook,* pp. 84, 85, 86 • M1–M2*, Family Letter

*See *Materials to Prepare,* p. 19.

Classroom Routines

Quick Images: Tens and Ones Show Image 1 from *Quick Images 1: Tens and Ones* (T69). Follow the basic *Quick Images* activity. Ask students to determine the total number of squares. Record an equation $20 + 5 = 25$ to represent the image. If a student saw the image as $30 - 5 = 25$ record that as well. Repeat for Images 2 and 3, recording an addition and subtraction equation for each image.

ACTIVITY

① What Is a Half?

35 MIN PAIRS CLASS

Explain to students that they are starting a new math unit about fractions. Ask students what they know about fractions and if they know any fractions.

The word *half* is commonly used, and your students most likely have experience sharing half of something. However, although many students know that halves involve two parts, they may not understand that the two parts must be equal.❶

Ask students what they can tell you about one half. Write students' ideas on the chart paper titled "What We Know About ½."❷

Students might say:

"Half a cookie."

"Half the class."

"Half a glass of milk."

For each example, emphasize that half involves two equal parts and that those two equal parts—when brought together—make one whole.❸

Note whether students give examples of both sets (half the class of 24 children, half the train of 32 cubes) and single objects (half of one cookie, half of one glass). Throughout the investigation, they will work with both.

One half is an example of a fraction. Fractions are used when we divide something into equal parts.

Write *one half* and ½ on the board and explain that this is how one half is written. Then direct students' attention to *Student Activity Book* pages 1–5.❹

Professional Development

❶ **Teacher Note:** Learning About Fractions, p. 77

Teaching Note

❷ **Save the Chart** Save the chart to look at during the final discussion of the unit.

Professional Development

❸ **Dialogue Box:** What Is One Half?, p. 83

Teaching Note

❹ **Linda and Ebony Share Everything** Linda and Ebony are twins who must share everything equally: sandwiches, stickers, marbles, and clay. Students color in each object or set to show Linda's share and Ebony's share. When the girls share a set, students say how many of the items each girl gets.

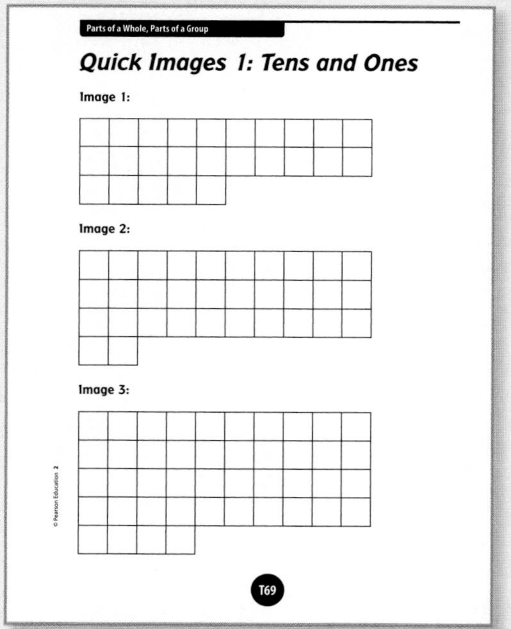

Parts of a Whole, Parts of a Group

Quick Images 1: Tens and Ones

Image 1:

Image 2:

Image 3:

T69

▲ Transparencies, T69

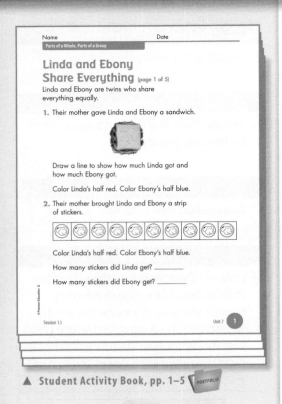

▲ Student Activity Book, pp. 1–5 [PORTFOLIO]

Read the first few problems aloud with the class. Students can work in pairs, but each student must respond in his or her own book. The *Student Activity Book* has 10 problems on 5 pages. Some students may do all 5 pages; others may work more slowly.

ONGOING ASSESSMENT: Observing Students at Work

Students divide objects and sets in half.

- **Do students draw a line to divide each object into two equal parts (Problems 1, 3, 5, 7, and 9)?**

- **Do students reason numerically to determine how many each girl gets or do they count for the problems about sets (Problems 2, 4, 6, 8, and 10)?**

DIFFERENTIATION: Supporting the Range of Learners

Intervention If students have difficulty finding half of the set of 10 stickers, ask them to draw a line that divides the strip into two equal parts. Alternatively, give students 10 tiles (representing the 10 stickers) for them to distribute between Linda and Ebony. Label 2 sheets of paper "Linda" and "Ebony" to help students keep track of the stickers distributed to each of the girls.

ELL Use visuals to aid English Language Learners' comprehension of the examples their classmates present during the discussion. As students explain examples, show and point out any that may be found in the classroom, such as a glass, or sketch a few examples on the board.

DISCUSSION

25 MIN CLASS

② Half of Objects/Half of Sets

Math Focus Points for Discussion

◆ Understanding that $\frac{1}{2}$ is one of two equal parts

◆ Finding one half of a set

◆ Showing one half of an object

Base this discussion on those problems that *all* students have worked on. Begin by sharing solutions to Problem 1.

For the first problem, Linda and Ebony cut their sandwich in half so that they could share it. Let's see how you divided the sandwich. What is the shape of their sandwich before dividing it? And what are the shapes of the two pieces after dividing it?

Students may have divided the sandwich in different ways.

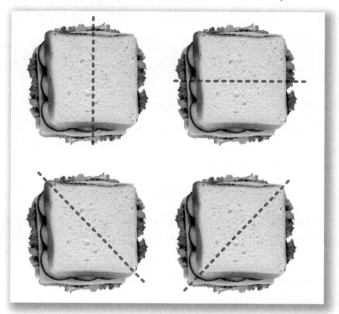

Students should see that there are different ways to divide the sandwich but that each way must cut the sandwich into two equal parts. Remind students of their work on symmetry in the beginning of the year. Objects that are symmetrical can be divided in half along lines of symmetry.

If all of your students completed Problem 3 or 5, have them share their solutions to these problems as well.

Next, share solutions to Problem 2. First, have students explain how they found the number of stickers each girl got. Then look at how they colored in each girl's share. Note that half of 10 can be represented in a variety of ways, as long as Linda and Ebony each get 5 stickers.

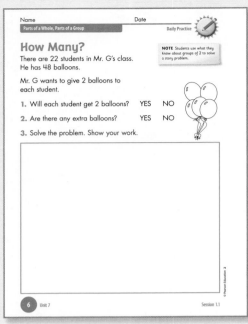

▲ **Student Activity Book, p. 6**

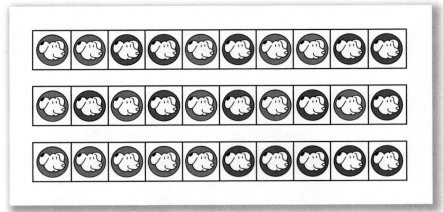

Some students may divide the strips of stickers in half by cutting each sticker in half. If students do this, acknowledge that it is also correct but pose the following question:

How could each girl get half the stickers and still get whole dog heads?

After solutions to both types of problems have been discussed, ask the class how the problems are the same and how they are different.

SESSION FOLLOW-UP

3 Daily Practice

 Daily Practice: For ongoing review, have students complete *Student Activity Book* page 6.

 Student Math Handbook: Students and families may use *Student Math Handbook* pages 84, 85, 86 for reference and review. See pages 92–94 in the back of this unit.

 Family Letter: Send home copies of the Family Letter (M1–M2).

Halves of Blocks and Balloon Bunches

Math Focus Points

◆ Determining whether a block is half of another block

◆ Solving problems about finding halves of quantities in different contexts

Today's Plan		Materials
ACTIVITY **① Introducing Geoblock and Balloon Activities**	15 MIN CLASS	• Geoblocks • Geoblocks: Rectangular Prism 8 cm x 4 cm x 4 cm; Cube 4 cm
MATH WORKSHOP **② Geoblocks and Balloons** **2A** Halves of Geoblocks **2B** Bunches of Balloons	45 MIN	**2A** • M4 ☑ • Student Activity Book, pp. 7–8 (p. 8 is optional) • Geoblocks **2B** • Student Activity Book, pp. 9–12 (pp. 11–12 are optional) • Connecting cubes (optional)
SESSION FOLLOW-UP **③ Daily Practice**		• Student Activity Book, p. 13 • Student Math Handbook, p. 86

*See Materials to Prepare, p. 19.

Classroom Routines

Today's Number: 15 Using Multiples of 5 and 10 and Subtraction As a whole class generate expressions for 15 using only subtraction and two numbers that are multiples of 5 or 10. For example: 30 — 15, 20 — 5 or 45 — 30. The 100 chart or number line will be a useful tool for some students. After several expressions have been generated, look at a series of expressions such as 20 — 5, 30 — 15 and 40 — 25 and ask students if they notice any patterns.

Math Note

① Geoblocks There are three Geoblocks that are half of the 4 cm x 8 cm x 4 cm rectangular prism— a 4 cm cube, a rectangular prism 2 cm x 8 cm x 4 cm, and a triangular prism 4 cm x 8 cm x 4 cm.

ACTIVITY

Introducing Geoblock and Balloon Activities

15 MIN CLASS

In the next three sessions, students work with halves and not halves of three different kinds of objects: three-dimensional objects (Geoblocks), two-dimensional objects (rectangles), and sets (bunches of balloons). In this session, they begin with Geoblocks and bunches of balloons.

First, describe the activity Halves of Geoblocks. Gather students in a circle around a set of Geoblocks. Students should be able to see all of the blocks in the set. Hold up the rectangular prism that measures 4 cm x 8 cm x 4 cm.

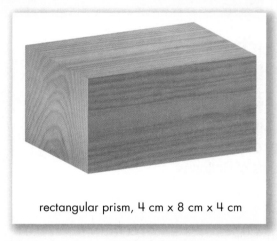

rectangular prism, 4 cm x 8 cm x 4 cm

Is there a Geoblock that is one half of this block?

Let a few students try to find such a block, or hold up a 4 cm cube and ask:

Is this block [hold up the cube] one half of this block [hold up the prism]? How can you prove it? Could there be a different block that is also one half of this block?

Have a student show that two cubes can be put together to make the prism.①

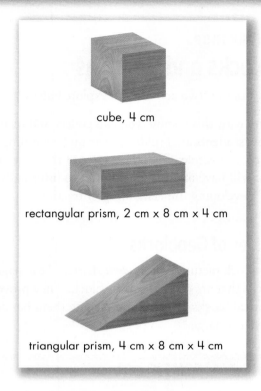

cube, 4 cm

rectangular prism, 2 cm x 8 cm x 4 cm

triangular prism, 4 cm x 8 cm x 4 cm

Assessment Checklist: Fractions as Equal Parts

Student	Finds ½ of a Whole • Divides a shape into equal parts • Identifies ½ of a rectangle or block	Finds ½ of a Set • Divides a set of objects into 2 equal sets • Identifies unequal situations	Identifies Parts Using Fractions • Labels parts of a divided shape using fractions

M4　Unit 7　　　　　　　　　　　　　　　　　　　Sessions 1.2, 1.3, 1.4, 2.1

© Pearson Education 2

▲ **Resource Masters, M4** ☑

Discuss the second activity, Bunches of Balloons.

On Saturday, Linda and Ebony will have a birthday. Some of their friends and relatives send them birthday balloons early. On Monday, Tuesday, Wednesday, Thursday, and Friday, Linda and Ebony share the balloons that come. For each day, you need to figure out whether Linda and Ebony can each get half of the balloons.

Let's do Monday together. On Monday, 7 balloons arrive. I want you to think about whether each girl can get half.

Students might say:

"It can't be 3 because 3 + 3 = 6. It can't be 4 because 4 + 4 = 8."

If a child suggests that $3\frac{1}{2} + 3\frac{1}{2} = 7$, point out that the girls cannot cut up a balloon. Explain to students that some days each girl will not get half and when they share the balloons that come on Monday, one girl gets 3 and the other gets 4.

Teaching Note

❷ **Assessment** Assessment Checklist: Fractions as Equal Parts (M4), is intended to help you think about how your students are making sense of fractions during the early part of this unit. While this checklist is connected to the benchmarks in this unit, students will be formally assessed on these benchmarks in the End-of-Unit Assessment in Session 2.6.

❸ **Geoblocks** Six students can share a set of Geoblocks for this activity.

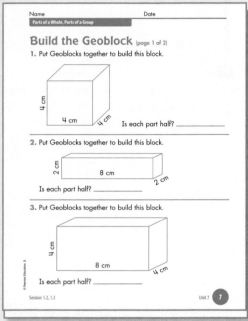

▲ Student Activity Book, pp. 7–8

MATH WORKSHOP

❷ # Geoblocks and Balloons

45 MIN

Students work on two activities to explore halves.

Beginning with this session, you can collect and record information about how students are building their understanding of fractions as equal parts of a whole. Over the course of this investigation and the next, you will have many opportunities to informally assess your students' developing understanding of fractions.❷

2A Halves of Geoblocks

INDIVIDUALS PAIRS

For each block pictured on *Student Activity Book* pages 7–8, students find blocks that are one half of the block. They prove this by putting two identical blocks together and placing them beside the Geoblock that is twice as large.❸

ONGOING ASSESSMENT: Observing Students at Work

Students find one half of a single object.

- **Can students find two blocks that, when brought together, make another block?**

- **Can students correctly identify which of the smaller blocks are half of the larger block and which are not?**

- **Do students find more than one block that is half of another block?**

DIFFERENTIATION: Supporting the Range of Learners

Extension If students complete *Student Activity Book* page 7, have them work on *Student Activity Book* page 8. If students finish page 8, challenge them to find all of the possible Geoblocks that are half of other blocks. If students find more than one block that is half of another block, you might ask the following:

- Do all of these blocks [point to all the blocks that the students found to be halves, then point to the block that the students were finding a half of] contain the same amount of wood, or does one block have more wood than the others?

This may be a difficult question for many students, so don't expect them to come to agreement about this.

Make sure English Language Learners understand the task they are to complete. Model the activity with them, doing one example yourself and then walking students through an example. If possible, pair an English Language Learner with a more fluent classmate who can provide assistance understanding the directions.

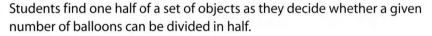

2B Bunches of Balloons

INDIVIDUALS   PAIRS

Students solve the problems on *Student Activity Book* pages 9–10.

ONGOING ASSESSMENT: Observing Students at Work

Students find one half of a set of objects as they decide whether a given number of balloons can be divided in half.

- **Are students able to identify which numbers can be divided in half? Of these numbers, can students say what half is?**

- **If a number cannot be divided in half, do students find the two closest values that add to that number? (For example, if there are 7 balloons, one girl gets 4 and the other gets 3.)**

- **Are students counting by ones or are they reasoning numerically?**

- **Do students keep track of whether Linda and Ebony have shared the balloons equally over the week?** Do they give one girl the extra balloon on Monday and the other girl the extra balloon on Thursday?

- **Are students able to add the five amounts accurately at the end of the week?**

DIFFERENTIATION: Supporting the Range of Learners

Intervention If students have difficulty with these problems, have them use cubes to represent balloons. They might write "Linda" and "Ebony" on different sheets of paper, count out the number of cubes, and then see whether the cubes can be distributed equally between the two girls.

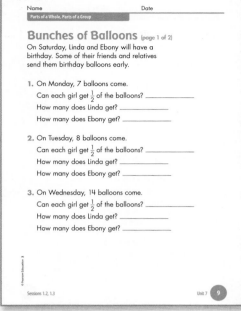

Name _____ Date _____
Parts of a Whole, Parts of a Group

Bunches of Balloons (page 1 of 2)
On Saturday, Linda and Ebony will have a birthday. Some of their friends and relatives send them birthday balloons early.

1. On Monday, 7 balloons come.
   Can each girl get $\frac{1}{2}$ of the balloons? _____
   How many does Linda get? _____
   How many does Ebony get? _____

2. On Tuesday, 8 balloons come.
   Can each girl get $\frac{1}{2}$ of the balloons? _____
   How many does Linda get? _____
   How many does Ebony get? _____

3. On Wednesday, 14 balloons come.
   Can each girl get $\frac{1}{2}$ of the balloons? _____
   How many does Linda get? _____
   How many does Ebony get? _____

Sessions 1.2, 1.3   Unit 7   9

▲ **Student Activity Book, p. 9**

Name _____ Date _____
Parts of a Whole, Parts of a Group

Bunches of Balloons (page 2 of 2)
4. On Thursday, 11 balloons come.
   Can each girl get $\frac{1}{2}$ of the balloons? _____
   How many does Linda get? _____
   How many does Ebony get? _____

5. On Friday, 20 balloons come.
   Can each girl get $\frac{1}{2}$ of the balloons? _____
   How many does Linda get? _____
   How many does Ebony get? _____

6. On Saturday they say, "It's hard to keep track of whose balloons are whose!" So they put all of their balloons together and add them up.
   How many balloons came that week? _____
   Can each girl get $\frac{1}{2}$ of the balloons? _____
   How many does Linda get? _____
   How many does Ebony get? _____

10   Unit 7   Sessions 1.2, 1.3

▲ **Student Activity Book, p. 10**

Student Activity Book, p. 11

Name _____ Date _____
Parts of a Whole, Parts of a Group

Sharing Pennies (page 1 of 2)
Linda and Ebony place all of the pennies they save in a jar. Sometimes they empty the jar, count out the pennies, and figure out how to share them equally. Then they put the pennies back.

1. On Monday, the girls counted 14 pennies in their jar.
   Can each girl get $\frac{1}{2}$ of the pennies? _____
   How many does Linda get? _____
   How many does Ebony get? _____

2. On Tuesday, they found 7 more pennies and added them to the jar. They counted all the pennies in the jar.
   Can each girl get $\frac{1}{2}$ of the pennies? _____
   How many does Linda get? _____
   How many does Ebony get? _____

3. On Wednesday, their sister gave them 9 pennies. They put them in the jar.
   Can each girl get $\frac{1}{2}$ of the pennies? _____
   How many does Linda get? _____
   How many does Ebony get? _____

Sessions 1.2, 1.3   Unit 7   11

▲ Student Activity Book, p. 11

Name _____ Date _____
Parts of a Whole, Parts of a Group

Sharing Pennies (page 2 of 2)
4. On Thursday, their mother added 6 pennies to their jar.
   Can each girl get $\frac{1}{2}$ of the pennies? _____
   How many does Linda get? _____
   How many does Ebony get? _____

5. On Friday, their father put 18 pennies in their jar.
   Can each girl get $\frac{1}{2}$ of the pennies? _____
   How many does Linda get? _____
   How many does Ebony get? _____

6. On Saturday, they counted up all of their pennies.
   How many pennies do they have? _____
   Show your work.

12   Unit 7   Sessions 1.2, 1.3

▲ Student Activity Book, p. 12

Extension If students complete *Student Activity Book* pages 9–10, have them work on *Student Activity Book* pages 11–12. On *Student Activity Book* pages 11–12, students determine whether a quantity of pennies can be divided in half and decide how many pennies each girl gets. The number of pennies to divide is larger than the number of balloons.

SESSION FOLLOW-UP
3 Daily Practice

Daily Practice: For reinforcement of this unit's content, have students complete *Student Activity Book* page 13.

Student Math Handbook: Students and families may use *Student Math Handbook* page 86 for reference and review. See pages 92–94 in the back of this unit.

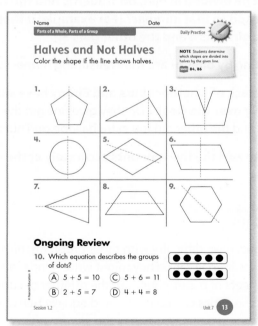

▲ Student Activity Book, p. 13

Halves of Blocks, Balloons, and Rectangles

Math Focus Points

◆ Determining whether a region is half of a given rectangle

◆ Determining whether a block is half of another block

◆ Solving problems about finding halves of quantities in different contexts

Today's Plan		Materials
ACTIVITY ①**Introducing Halves/Not Halves of Rectangles**	10 MIN CLASS	• T70 –T71 ; Piece A from M10* • Chart: Halves and Not Halves of Rectangles*
MATH WORKSHOP ②**Halves of Blocks, Balloons, and Rectangles Workshop** ②A Halves of Geoblock ②B Bunches of Balloons ②C Halves/Not Halves of Rectangles	30 MIN	②A • Materials from Session 1.2 ②B • Materials from Session 1.2 ②C • *Student Activity Book*, pp. 14–15 • M10* • Crayons
DISCUSSION ③**Halves of a Bunch**	20 MIN CLASS	• *Student Activity Book*, pp. 9–10 (from Session 1.2) • Chart: "Halves of Bunches"*
SESSION FOLLOW-UP ④**Daily Practice**		• *Student Activity Book*, p. 16 • M5–M6*, Family Letter • *Student Math Handbook*, p. 86

*See *Materials to Prepare*, p. 19.

Classroom Routines

What Time Is It? Counting the Minutes Using The Clocks (M7), have students divide the clock into quarters by first dividing the clock in half (drawing a line between the 12 and the 6) and then drawing a line between the 3 and 9. Students then count the number of minutes in each quarter, labeling the 15, 30, and 45 minutes. Post the time 2:45 on the board and have students set their clocks to that time.

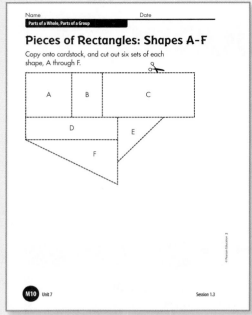

▲ Resource Masters, M10

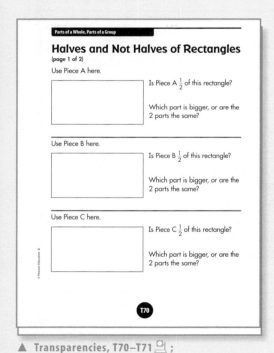

▲ Transparencies, T70–T71 ;

Resource Masters, M8–M9

10 MIN   CLASS

ACTIVITY

① Introducing Halves/Not Halves of Rectangles

Remind the group of the activity they did two sessions ago when Linda and Ebony shared a sandwich.

We have seen that there are different ways to divide rectangles in half. Think back to when Linda and Ebony shared a sandwich and needed to cut it in half.

Draw on the overhead a rectangle (or point to the rectangle on the chart you prepared), and ask the class what shape the sandwich was.

In our new workshop activity, you will look at different parts of a rectangle and decide whether each part is half or not half.

Place the transparency of Halves and Not Halves of Rectangles (T70–T71) on the overhead or, alternatively, post the chart "Halves and Not Halves of Rectangles" that you prepared. Then take Piece A, which was cut from Pieces of Rectangles: Shapes A–F (M10) out of the bucket and hold it up for students to see. Place Piece A on the first rectangle on the transparency or on the rectangle on the chart and draw a line to mark off Piece A, dividing the rectangle into two parts. Shade in the left part and label it "A."

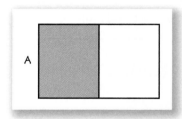

Is Piece A half of the rectangle? Which part is bigger or are they the same?

As students offer their ideas, listen for an explanation that includes that the two parts are equal, making Piece A half of the rectangle. Highlight this for the class and record it on the transparency or chart.

Halves of Blocks, Balloons, and Rectangles Workshop

30 MIN

Students work on three activities to explore halves and not halves. Make sure that students are prepared to discuss Activity 2, Bunches of Balloons, by the end of the session.

2A Halves of Geoblocks

PAIRS

For complete details about this activity, see Session 1.2, pages 28–29.

2B Bunches of Balloons

PAIRS

For complete details about this activity, see Session 1.2, pages 29–30.

2C Halves/Not Halves of Rectangles

PAIRS

Students place cutout pieces from Pieces of Rectangles: Shapes A–F (M10) on the rectangles on *Student Activity Book* pages 14–15, and determine whether each piece is $\frac{1}{2}$ of the rectangle. Using two different colors, they shade in the two parts of the rectangle and answer the question. Which part is bigger, or are the 2 parts the same?

There are six different pieces marked with a letter, A through F. Place each piece on the rectangle and then trace it so that you can color in the two parts of the rectangle. Then decide whether the piece is half or not half. If it is not half, say which part is bigger.

ONGOING ASSESSMENT: Observing Students at Work

Students compare fractional parts to a whole and determine which are $\frac{1}{2}$ of the whole.

● **Can students correctly identify which pieces are half of the rectangle and which are not?**

Name _____ Date _____

Parts of a Whole, Parts of a Group

Halves and Not Halves of Rectangles
(page 2 of 2)

Use Piece D here.

Is Piece D $\frac{1}{2}$ of this rectangle?

Which part is bigger, or are the 2 parts the same?

Use Piece E here.

Is Piece E $\frac{1}{2}$ of this rectangle?

Which part is bigger, or are the 2 parts the same?

Use Piece F here.

Is Piece F $\frac{1}{2}$ of this rectangle?

Which part is bigger, or are the 2 parts the same?

Session 1.3   Unit 7 M9

▲ Resource Masters, M9; T71

Name _____ Date _____

Parts of a Whole, Parts of a Group

Halves and Not Halves of Rectangles (page 1 of 2)

Use Piece A here.

Is Piece A $\frac{1}{2}$ of this rectangle?

Which part is bigger, or are the 2 parts the same? _____

Use Piece B here.

Is Piece B $\frac{1}{2}$ of this rectangle?

Which part is bigger, or are the 2 parts the same? _____

Use Piece C here.

Is Piece C $\frac{1}{2}$ of this rectangle?

Which part is bigger, or are the 2 parts the same? _____

14 Unit 7   Sessions 1.3, 1.4

▲ Student Activity Book, pp. 14–15

DIFFERENTIATION: Supporting the Range of Learners

Extension If students are clear about which pieces are half (A, D, and F) and which are not (B, C, and E), you might ask the following:

- If these rectangles were sandwiches cut in half, would this half-sandwich [point to Piece D] have the same amount as this half-sandwich [point to Piece F] or this half-sandwich [point to Piece A]? Or does one half-sandwich have more than the others?

This may be a difficult question for many students, so don't expect them to come to agreement about this.

DISCUSSION

3 Halves of a Bunch

20 MIN CLASS

Math Focus Points for Discussion

◆ Solving problems about finding halves of quantities in different contexts

Post the chart "Halves of Bunches" to organize the discussion of *Student Activity Book* pages 9–10.

Let's start with the first question. On Monday, when there are 7 balloons, can the girls split the balloons in half?

As students share their answers, fill in the chart.

Halves of Bunches

Number of Balloons	"Split in Half?"	How Many Does Each Girl Get?
7	No	4 + 3
8	Yes	4 + 4
14	Yes	7 + 7
11	No	5 + 6
20	Yes	10 + 10

After the chart is complete for the values through Friday, ask:

What do you notice about the numbers that work and the numbers that don't work? Share what you notice with those sitting next to you.

After a few moments, bring the whole group back together to share their observations. Students might begin by talking about specific numbers but then generalize to include all of the numbers in the chart: those that can be split in half are doubles and are even numbers; those that cannot be split in half are near-doubles and are odd numbers.

If students argue that cutting the odd piece in half can split an odd number, acknowledge that this is correct. Point out that some objects can be split in half while others, such as balloons, cannot. Ask students to suggest what Linda and Ebony might share so that if they had 7 of them, they could each get half. (This will be the topic of discussion in the next session.)

Next ask students to focus on why one half of 8 is different than one half of 10.

In these balloon problems you were finding one half of a bunch of balloons. So if you were always finding $\frac{1}{2}$ why did you get different numbers?

Collect several students' ideas and listen for reasoning that different size bunches result in halves of different sizes.

If there is time, conclude the session by having students share their strategies for finding the total number of balloons the two girls received during the week.

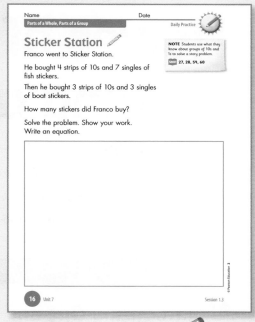

▲ **Student Activity Book, p. 16**

SESSION FOLLOW-UP
4 Daily Practice

 Daily Practice: For ongoing review, have students complete *Student Activity Book* page 16.

 Student Math Handbook: Students and families may use *Student Math Handbook* page 86 for reference and review. See pages 92–94 in the back of this unit.

 Family Letter: Send home copies of the Family Letter (M5–M6).

Halves of Rectangles and Sharing a Picnic Workshop

Math Focus Points

◆ Solving problems that result in mixed numbers

◆ Learning the terms and notation for mixed numbers (e.g., $1\frac{1}{2}$)

◆ Finding equal parts of a whole and naming them with fractions ($\frac{1}{2}$ as one of two equal parts)

Vocabulary

one and a half
two and a half

Today's Plan		Materials
ACTIVITY **① Introducing One and a Half, Two and a Half**	10 MIN CLASS	
MATH WORKSHOP **② Halves of Rectangles and Sharing a Picnic** ②Ⓐ Halves/Not Halves of Rectangles ②Ⓑ Going on a Picnic	35 MIN	②Ⓐ • Materials from Session 1.2 ②Ⓑ • *Student Activity Book*, pp. 17–18 • Connecting cubes
DISCUSSION **③ Halves of a Rectangle**	15 MIN	• *Student Activity Book*, pp. 14–15 (from Session 1.3) • T70–T71 ; M10 • Chart: Halves and Not Halves of Rectangles (from Session 1.3)
SESSION FOLLOW-UP **④ Daily Practice and Homework**		• *Student Activity Book*, pp. 19–20 • *Student Math Handbook*, pp. 84, 85, 86, 92

Classroom Routines

How Many Pockets? Using a Class List to Add Distribute a class list to each student. Students record each other's pocket data on the class list as it is announced. Once all the data has been collected, students calculate the total number of pockets the class is wearing. Before students begin to calculate, discuss some strategies they might use (e.g., looking for groups of ten, combining numbers they know, etc.). As students finish, have them discuss their work in pairs.

ACTIVITY

Introducing One and a Half, Two and a Half

10 MIN   CLASS

Up until now, Linda and Ebony have been sharing sets of objects that cannot be broken. Introducing sets that contain objects that can be divided in half allows you to show students the notation for mixed numbers (e.g., $1\frac{1}{2}$).

In the last session, Linda and Ebony were sharing balloons. Because a single balloon cannot be split in half, sometimes the twins can't share the balloons equally. If Linda and Ebony are given 3 balloons, can each girl get half? (*No, one girl must get 1 balloon and the other girl gets 2.*) But let's say that their friend gave them 3 balls of clay, and we know that a ball of clay can be cut in half. How much clay would each girl get if they shared 3 balls of clay?

Because a ball of clay can be cut in half, each girl will get $1\frac{1}{2}$ balls of clay. Have several students explain how they think about it, and ask at least one child to draw a picture for everyone to see.

Because the terms sound so similar, students often think that *one and a half* is the same as *one half*. Ask a question to have students clarify the distinction.

Is one and a half the same as one half?

Students might say:

"One and a half means 'you have one whole thing and also one half.'"

Write on the board *one and a half* and *$1\frac{1}{2}$*.

Ask students to explain why we write "one and a half" as "$1\frac{1}{2}$."

When we write the number *one and a half,* we first write the number *1.* That's for the whole ball we have. Then we write $\frac{1}{2}$ next to it, and that's for the half ball we have.

Let's look at another number. Let's say, instead, a friend gave the twins 5 balls of clay. After they divided it, each girl got two and a half balls of clay. How do you think we would write *two and a half*? (*$2\frac{1}{2}$*)

Ask two or three students to go to the board and show how they would write two and a half. Have them explain why it is written that way.

What does the *2* mean? What does the $\frac{1}{2}$ mean?

Going on a Picnic (page 1 of 2)

Linda and Ebony are going on a picnic, so their mother packed a lunch for them.

1. They have 3 sandwiches. They share the sandwiches evenly. How many sandwiches does each girl get?

2. They have 5 pieces of cheese. They share the cheese evenly. How many pieces of cheese does each girl get?

3. They have 9 strawberries. They share the strawberries evenly. How many strawberries does each girl get?

4. They have 11 carrot sticks. They share the carrot sticks evenly. How many carrot sticks does each girl get?

5. They have 7 celery sticks. They share the celery sticks evenly. How many celery sticks does each girl get?

▲ **Student Activity Book, p. 17**

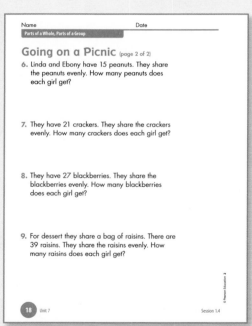

Going on a Picnic (page 2 of 2)

6. Linda and Ebony have 15 peanuts. They share the peanuts evenly. How many peanuts does each girl get?

7. They have 21 crackers. They share the crackers evenly. How many crackers does each girl get?

8. They have 27 blackberries. They share the blackberries evenly. How many blackberries does each girl get?

9. For dessert they share a bag of raisins. There are 39 raisins. They share the raisins evenly. How many raisins does each girl get?

▲ **Student Activity Book, p. 18**

MATH WORKSHOP

② Halves of Rectangles and Sharing a Picnic

35 MIN

Make sure that students are prepared to discuss *Student Activity Book* pages 14–15 by the end of the session. Those students who have completed this activity should work on Going on a Picnic, *Student Activity Book* pages 17–18.

②A Halves/Not Halves of Rectangles

PAIRS

For complete details about this activity, see Session 1.3, pages 33–34.

Students determine which pieces are halves and which are not halves.

②B Going on a Picnic

PAIRS

On *Student Activity Book* pages 17–18, Linda and Ebony each get half of everything their mother packed in their picnic basket: 3 sandwiches, 5 pieces of cheese, and so on. This is a 2-page activity, but many students may only get through the first page.

ONGOING ASSESSMENT: Observing Students at Work

Students find halves of odd numbers, which requires that they represent the results as mixed numbers.

• **How do students find half of an odd number?** Do they reason numerically or do they count?

• **Are students able to represent the results as mixed numbers?**

DIFFERENTIATION: Supporting the Range of Learners

Intervention If students have difficulty with these problems, have them use cubes to represent food items. They might write "Linda" and "Ebony" on different sheets of paper, count out the number of cubes, and then distribute them equally between the two girls. Because the numbers are odd, when they get to the last cube, students will need to imagine cutting it in half to share between the girls.

Extension If students work quickly through *Student Activity Book* page 17, have them work on *Student Activity Book* page 18, which challenges students with larger numbers.

ELL Once again, take time to explain key terms and vocabulary to English Language Learners. Keep in mind that English Language Learners may be familiar with the math concepts being discussed but simply lack the language in English to express their ideas or understand the directions. Providing visuals is an efficient means of helping English Language Learners understand tasks more readily.

DISCUSSION

3 Halves of a Rectangle

15 MIN   CLASS

Math Focus Points for Discussion

◆ Finding equal parts of a whole and naming them with fractions ($\frac{1}{2}$ as one of two equal parts)

Students come to the discussion with completed *Student Activity Book* pages 14–15.

Have students explain how they know that Piece B is not $\frac{1}{2}$ of the rectangle.

Which of the pieces that you worked with is one half of the rectangle?

If there is any disagreement that Pieces A, D, and F are halves and that Pieces B, C, and E are not halves, have students explain why they think the piece is or is not one half. Use this as an opportunity to review what makes a half.

Students can use the Pieces of Rectangles: Shapes A–F (M10) and the overhead projector and transparencies of Halves and Not Halves of Rectangles (T70–T71) or the chart "Halves and Not Halves

---

Parts of a Whole, Parts of a Group

Halves and Not Halves of Rectangles
(page 1 of 2)

Use Piece A here.

Is Piece A $\frac{1}{2}$ of this rectangle?

Which part is bigger, or are the 2 parts the same?

Use Piece B here.

Is Piece B $\frac{1}{2}$ of this rectangle?

Which part is bigger, or are the 2 parts the same?

Use Piece C here.

Is Piece C $\frac{1}{2}$ of this rectangle?

Which part is bigger, or are the 2 parts the same?

T70

▲ Transparencies, T70

Parts of a Whole, Parts of a Group

Halves and Not Halves of Rectangles
(page 2 of 2)

Use Piece D here.

Is Piece D $\frac{1}{2}$ of this rectangle?

Which part is bigger, or are the 2 parts the same?

Use Piece E here.

Is Piece E $\frac{1}{2}$ of this rectangle?

Which part is bigger, or are the 2 parts the same?

Use Piece F here.

Is Piece F $\frac{1}{2}$ of this rectangle?

Which part is bigger, or are the 2 parts the same?

T71

▲ Transparencies, T71

▲ Student Activity Book, p. 19

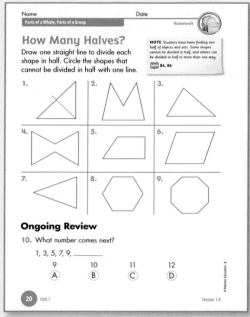

▲ Student Activity Book, p. 20

of Rectangles" as they explain.

If any students have noticed that two copies of Piece E together make up one half, explore this with the class. If no students bring up this idea, you may choose to introduce it yourself.

I heard that in one class, a second grader took two copies of Piece E and put them together. (Hold up two copies of Piece E.) This student said that two copies of Piece E make up one half of the rectangle. What do you think of that?

Give students a chance to look at their own *Student Activity Book* page 15, on which they have traced Piece E.

Do you agree? If you had another copy of Piece E, would the two copies of Piece E make one half of the rectangle?

If students think that they can show it, have them approach the overhead and arrange the pieces to mark off one half. Ask whether the rest of the class agrees.

Then take the pieces off and place one copy of Piece E at the other end of the rectangle. Again, ask a student to approach the overhead and arrange the second copy of Piece E that shows one half.

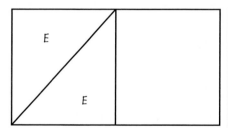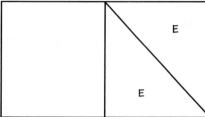

Unless students raise ideas, do not try to push too far ahead at this time. In the next Investigation, students will work on $\frac{1}{4}$, $\frac{2}{4}$, and $\frac{3}{4}$.

SESSION FOLLOW-UP
4 Daily Practice and Homework

Daily Practice: For ongoing review, have students complete *Student Activity Book* page 19.

Homework: Students practice their understanding of halves on *Student Activity Book* page 20.

Student Math Handbook: Students and families may use *Student Math Handbook* pages 84, 85, 86, 92 for reference and

Mathematical Emphases

Rational Numbers Understanding fractions as equal parts of a whole

Math Focus Points

◆ Seeing different ways to make fourths of a square

◆ Recognizing the equivalence of different fourths of the same object

◆ Identifying halves, thirds, and fourths of regions

◆ Identifying and naming fractional parts that have numerators greater than 1 (e.g., $\frac{2}{3}, \frac{2}{4}, \frac{3}{4}$)

Rational Numbers Understanding fractions as equal parts of a group

Math Focus Points

◆ Finding thirds and fourths of sets

◆ Finding fractions of sets

Rational Numbers Using terms and notation

Math Focus Points

◆ Learning the term *one fourth* and the notation $\frac{1}{4}$

◆ Learning the term *one third* and the notation $\frac{1}{3}$

◆ Learning the terms and notation for fractions that contain more than one part (e.g., $\frac{2}{3}, \frac{2}{4}$, and $\frac{3}{4}$)

Halves, Thirds, and Fourths

	Student Activity Book	Student Math Handbook	Professional Development: Read Ahead of Time	
SESSION 2.1 p. 46				
Fourths of a Square Students fold a square piece of paper to make halves and fourths. They investigate different ways to fold a square to make fourths and compare differently-shaped fourths.	21	87	• **Dialogue Box:** Fourths: Same or Different?, p. 85	
SESSION 2.2 p. 53				
Thirds of a Flag Illustrating fractions with flags from different countries, the teacher defines thirds for the class. The class then creates a fractions chart about fractions they know—$\frac{1}{2}$, $\frac{1}{3}$, and $\frac{1}{4}$. Students color in regions of a flag and write what fraction of the flag each color represents.	22–26	86, 87, 90		
SESSION 2.3 p. 58				
More Fraction Flags The teacher illustrates what $\frac{2}{3}$, $\frac{2}{4}$, and $\frac{3}{4}$ mean by coloring flags that are divided into thirds or fourths. Students color in more fraction flags, identifying what fraction of a flag each color represents.	27–31	86, 87, 88, 89, 90, 91		
SESSION 2.4 p. 64				
Fraction Flag Posters The class creates "Fraction Flag" posters, sorting their flags by the fractions illustrated.	27–30, 32	86, 87, 88, 89, 90, 91	• **Dialogue Box:** Talking About Fraction Flags, p. 87	

Classroom Routines See page 14 for an overview.

Quick Images	Today's Number
• **T73**, *Quick Images 2: Tens and Ones* 🖳 Cut apart the images.	• **M23**, *Today's Number* Make copies. (1 per student)
• **T74**, *Quick Images 3: Tens and Ones* 🖳 Cut apart the images.	• **T77**, *Today's Number* 🖳
	What Time Is It?
	• **Student clocks** (1 per pair)

Materials to Gather	Materials to Prepare
• **Square pieces of paper**, about 8.5″ x 8.5″ (3 per student) • **Crayons** (as needed) • **4 quarters** • **Chart paper** • **Scissors** (as needed) • **Connecting cubes** (as needed) • **Tiles** (as needed) • **Clock**	• **Chart paper** Title a piece of chart paper "Different Ways to Show Fourths."
• **World map** (optional) • **Flag books and posters** (optional)	• **T75, Flags in Halves, Thirds, and Fourths** 🖳 Color the top half of the first flag white and the bottom half red. Color the second flag white, blue, and red, in that order from top to bottom. Color the last flag red, blue, yellow, and green, in that order from top to bottom. Refer to page 54. OR **Chart paper** Draw 3 rectangles and duplicate the flags on the transparency of Flags in Halves, Thirds, and Fourths (T75). • **Chart paper** Create a 4-column chart titled "Fractions." Leave the first column unlabeled, label the second "Number of Equal Pieces," label the third "Names of Parts," and label the last "Fraction." In the first column, first row is a rectangle divided in half vertically with the first half shaded in; in the second row is a rectangle divided in three equal parts with the last part shaded in; and in the last row is a rectangle divided in four equal parts with the first part shaded in. See page 55.
• **Chart: "Fractions"** (from Session 2.2) • **Crayons** (as needed)	• **T76, Flags in Thirds and Fourths** 🖳 Color the first and last third of the first flag green and the middle third white. Color the top two fourths of the second flag yellow, the third fourth blue, and the bottom fourth red. Color the top two fourths of the last flag green, the bottom left-hand fourth green, and the bottom right-hand fourth blue. Refer to pages 59 and 61. OR **Chart paper** Title chart paper "Thirds and Fourths." Draw 3 rectangles and duplicate the flags on the transparency of Flags in Thirds and Fourths (T76).
• **Crayons** (as needed) • **Tape**	• **M15–M22, Fraction Flags** Make copies and cut in half (3 of each). • **Chart paper** Label seven sheets of paper with one of the following: "$\frac{1}{2}$ and $\frac{1}{2}$," "$\frac{1}{3}$ and $\frac{1}{3}$ and $\frac{1}{3}$," "$\frac{2}{3}$ and $\frac{1}{3}$," "$\frac{1}{4}$ and $\frac{1}{4}$ and $\frac{1}{4}$ and $\frac{1}{4}$," "$\frac{2}{4}$ and $\frac{1}{4}$ and $\frac{1}{4}$," "$\frac{2}{4}$ and $\frac{2}{4}$," "$\frac{3}{4}$ and $\frac{1}{4}$."

🖳 Overhead Transparency

Halves, Thirds, and Fourths,
continued

	Student Activity Book	Student Math Handbook	Professional Development: Read Ahead of Time	
SESSION 2.5 p. 68				
Sharing Among Friends Students are introduced to story problems in which three or four children share a set of objects equally, dividing the set into thirds or fourths.	33–36	87, 90	• **Dialogue Box:** Thirds and Fourths of Sets, p. 89	
SESSION 2.6 p. 73				
End-of-Unit Assessment Students solve three problems to assess their ability to identify fractional parts of a whole, find $\frac{1}{2}$ of a set of objects, and assess their understanding of fractions as equal parts of a whole.	33–35, 37	84, 86–88, 90	• **Teacher Note:** End-of-Unit Assessment, p. 79	

Materials to Gather	Materials to Prepare
• **Connecting cubes** (35 per pair)	
• **Chart: "What We Know About $\frac{1}{2}$"** (from Session 1.1)	• **M24–M25, End-of-Unit Assessment** Make copies. (1 per student)

Fourths of a Square

Math Focus Points

◆ Seeing different ways to make fourths of a square

◆ Learning the term *one fourth* and the notation $\frac{1}{4}$

◆ Recognizing the equivalence of different fourths of the same object

Vocabulary

fraction
one fourth
one quarter
fourths

Today's Plan | Materials

1 ACTIVITY
Folding and Folding Again
30 MIN INDIVIDUALS CLASS
- Square pieces of paper, about 8.5" x 8.5" (3 per student); crayons (as needed); 4 quarters; clock; chart: "Different Ways to Show Fourths"*
- M4* (Session 1.2) ☑

2 ACTIVITY
Same or Different?
20 MIN INDIVIDUALS PAIRS
- Square pieces of paper, folded (from Activity 1); scissors (as needed); connecting cubes (as needed); tiles (as needed)

3 DISCUSSION
Comparing Fourths
10 MIN CLASS
- Chart: "Different Ways to Show Fourths"

4 SESSION FOLLOW-UP
Daily Practice
- *Student Activity Book*, p. 21
- *Student Math Handbook*, p. 87

*See *Materials to Prepare*, p. 43.

Classroom Routines

Quick Images: Tens and Ones Show Image 1 from *Quick Images 2: Tens and Ones* (T73). Follow the basic *Quick Images* activity. Ask students to determine the total number of squares. Record the equation, $30 + 9 = 39$, to represent the image. If a student saw the image as $40 - 1 = 39$ record that as well. Repeat for Images 2 and 3, recording an addition and subtraction equation for each image.

ACTIVITY
Folding and Folding Again

30 MIN INDIVIDUALS CLASS

Distribute one square piece of paper to each student.

Today we're going to look at the fractions we get when we fold paper. We'll start out by looking at halves. You're going to fold your square in half. You'll fold it so that the crease makes two equal pieces.

Before students fold their squares, ask them to show with their fingers, just for themselves, where the crease will be. After visualizing it this way, students should fold their papers.❶

After students have folded the square, ask them to open it up again and look at the halves.

Did your fold divide the square into two equal triangles? Do you have two halves? What shape are your halves?

Have one student hold up his or her square for all to see.

[Juanita] folded her square into two equal pieces. She folded her square into halves. Who folded the square like [Juanita]?

Have students raise their hands if their folds look like the one shown. Then have students who folded differently hold up their squares for everyone to see.

Most students will see these two ways to divide a square:

One results in two rectangles, the other in two triangles.

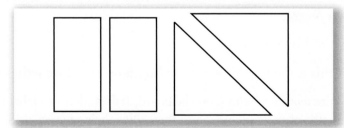

Rotating or flipping these figures produces slightly different results. Some students may consider these different ways to make half; others will see them as the same.❷ ❸

Teaching Notes

❶ **Folding Paper** If you anticipate that some students will have trouble folding the square, have them show you with their fingers where the crease will be and then fold the square for them.

❷ **Developing Ideas** Continue to informally assess your students' developing understanding of fractions throughout this investigation. Use Assessment Checklist: Fractions as Equal Parts (M4) to record your observations.

Math Note

❸ **Other Ways to Divide a Square** There are still other ways to divide a square in half. In the example below, both pieces are congruent halves of a square.

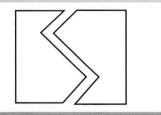

Unless students raise this as a possibility, do not bring it into the discussion. Instead, concentrate on vertical, horizontal, and diagonal folds.

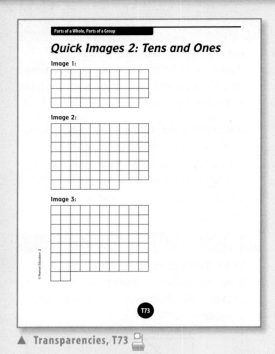

Parts of a Whole, Parts of a Group

Quick Images 2: Tens and Ones

Image 1:

Image 2:

Image 3:

T73

▲ **Transparencies, T73**

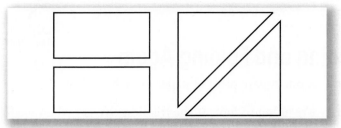

After students have looked at different ways to divide the square in half, ask them to repeat the first step and fold the square in half again.

Now, you have all folded your squares in half, so you're looking at one half of the square. What do you think will happen if you take that one half and fold it in half again? What do you think it will look like?

Before they fold the paper again, ask students to describe what they think the paper will look like.

When the square is folded over a second time, folding the half into halves, the original square is folded into fourths. After students have folded the half into halves, ask them how many parts they think they will find when they open up the square. Also ask them what shape those pieces will be. Then have them open up their squares to check their predictions.

How many pieces does your square have now? Are they equal? Does anyone know what each piece is called?

Record students' ideas on the board.

When something is divided into four equal pieces, each piece is called *one fourth*.

Write $\frac{1}{2}$ on the board.

If this is the way we write *one half*, how would we write *one fourth*?

Write *one fourth* and $\frac{1}{4}$ on the board. Ask students to label each of the fourths of their square $\frac{1}{4}$ and then color their squares, using a different color for each fourth.

We sometimes use another word to mean the same thing. We can also call each part *one quarter*. *One quarter* is the same as *one fourth*. Have you heard these words before?

Students may mention that quarters are 25-cent coins. Ask them whether they know how many pennies or cents a quarter is worth.

There are 25 pennies in one quarter and 100 pennies in one dollar.

Write 25¢ + 25¢ + 25¢ + 25¢ = 100¢ on the board. Ask students why 25¢ is called a quarter.

Show students four quarters and explain that 25¢ is one fourth of a dollar.

Students may also mention time and refer to a quarter of an hour. Ask them how long a quarter hour is and why it is called a quarter hour. Here, again, point out that a quarter of an hour is the same as one fourth of an hour, or 15 minutes. Four quarter hours make up one hour. Show the class a quarter hour on the clock.❹

Have students focus again on their squares.

Let's look at the different ways you made **fourths** *when you folded your paper.*

In the same way that you looked at halves, ask one student to show how he or she made fourths and then ask students to raise their hands if they did it the same way. Then ask whether anyone did it differently.

Expect students to show the following three ways to make fourths. Again, some students may think they have found another way by rotating the square.

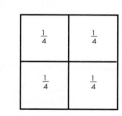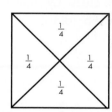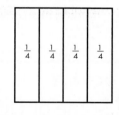

If the class doesn't come up with all three ways, challenge students to find the other way(s).

We have found two ways to fold the square into fourths, but there is still one more way. Can you find it?

Tape a sample of each way to make fourths onto the chart labeled "Different Ways to Show Fourths."

Distribute another square paper to each student.

You have all folded your squares to look like one of these ways to make fourths. Now I want you to fold this new square a different way to look like one of these other ways to make fourths.

As students finish showing fourths another way, remind them to label the fourths. Then give them another square to try yet another way.❺

Teaching Notes

❹ **Different Wholes** Be aware that in this discussion of a quarter of a dollar and a quarter of an hour, students are broaching a difficult idea: a quarter of a dollar is 25¢, but a quarter of an hour is 15 minutes. When working with fractions, it is important to pay attention to the whole. In the contexts of time and money, the wholes are different quantities—a dollar is 100 cents and an hour is 60 minutes—and while $\frac{1}{4}$ of 100 is a different quantity than $\frac{1}{4}$ of 60, both represent $\frac{1}{4}$ of the whole. Differentiating between these two ideas about fractions and what they represent is complex and something students will work on in subsequent grades.

❺ **Managing Class Time** Some students may benefit from spending the rest of the session working on this activity, while others will be ready to move on to the next activity. Decide on the best way to use these 60 minutes for your class. If you choose to spend the rest of the class time on Folding and Folding Again, then skip Same or Different and continue on to Session 2.2 for the next lesson.

Professional Development

⊙ **Dialogue Box:** Fourths: Same or Different?, p. 85

ONGOING ASSESSMENT: Observing Students at Work

Students fold a square piece of paper into fourths.

- **Do students recognize that two folds result in sectioning their papers into four parts?**

- **Do students fold their papers to make four equal parts?**

- **Can students fold their papers in different ways to make fourths?**

DIFFERENTIATION: Supporting the Range of Learners

Intervention Some students may have difficulty with this task because it involves developed fine motor and visual skills. It may be more appropriate for some students to draw the fourths or to tell you or a partner how they would like the paper folded.

ELL Before this activity, point out examples of vocabulary words, including fold, crease, equal, pieces, and shape using objects in the classroom. To show fold, use a piece of notebook paper, and fold it in half. Point to each piece and say: These are the same size. They are equal pieces. Explain crease by showing students the crease from folding in an envelope or folder.

ACTIVITY

20 MIN INDIVIDUALS PAIRS

2 Same or Different?

Students now compare different-looking fourths of the same object: Is one piece larger than the other, or are they the same?

If we think of these pieces of paper as sandwiches and we cut them into fourths three different ways, would all of the fourths be the same size or would they be different? If I gave you this piece [point to one of the smaller squares on the square that was divided into 4 squares] or this piece [point to one of the rectangles in the square that was divided into 4 vertical rectangles], would one be bigger or would they be the same size?

Tell students that they can use a variety of tools to explore this question. Some students may cut up the fourths to transform one shape into another. Other students may cover the fourths with cubes or tiles to show that they have equal area. Still others may lay one shape over another to compare the portion that extends beyond the edge of the smaller shape.⊙

The student proves the equivalence of different representations of fourths of the same object.

ONGOING ASSESSMENT: Observing Students at Work

Students explore whether a fourth of a sandwich cut one way is the same size as a fourth cut another way.

- **How do students approach this question?** Do they cut one $\frac{1}{4}$-piece into parts and rearrange the parts to fit over another $\frac{1}{4}$-piece? Do they cover one $\frac{1}{4}$-piece with tiles and show that another $\frac{1}{4}$-piece is covered with the same number of tiles?

- **Do students come to the conclusion that fourths of a given square are the same size, even if they have different shapes?**

10 MIN   CLASS

DISCUSSION
③ Comparing Fourths

Math Focus Points for Discussion

◆ Recognizing the equivalence of different fourths of the same object

Draw students' attention to the chart labeled "Different Ways to Show Fourths."

What do you think? Which way do you get more: cutting your sandwich this way [point to the square showing fourths as long rectangles] and taking $\frac{1}{4}$, or cutting your sandwich this way [point to the square showing fourths as smaller squares] and taking $\frac{1}{4}$?

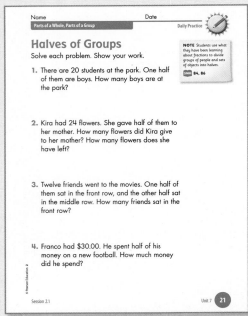

▲ **Student Activity Book, p. 21**

This may be a difficult question for many students, so do not expect them to come to agreement about this. However, it may be useful to pose the question and examine students' responses.

Some students will explain that, even though the pieces are different shapes, they have the same amount of sandwich. Have students share their proofs.

Some students will be able to see that by cutting one $\frac{1}{4}$-piece in half and rearranging the parts, they can cover the other $\frac{1}{4}$-piece.

Many students will find it more difficult to compare the triangular-shaped $\frac{1}{4}$ piece with either the square-shaped $\frac{1}{4}$ piece or the long rectangular-shaped $\frac{1}{4}$ piece.

SESSION FOLLOW-UP

4 Daily Practice

 Daily Practice: For reinforcement of this unit's content, have students complete *Student Activity Book* page 21.

 Student Math Handbook: Students and families may use *Student Math Handbook* page 87 for reference and review. See pages 92–94 in the back of this unit.

Thirds of a Flag

Math Focus Points

◆ Learning the term *one third* and the notation $\frac{1}{3}$

◆ Identifying halves, thirds, and fourths of regions

Vocabulary

one third

Today's Plan		Materials
ACTIVITY **①** A Third of a Flag	🕐 20 MIN 👪 CLASS	• *Student Activity Book*, pp. 22–25 • Chart: "Flags in Halves, Thirds, and Fourths"*; world map (optional); chart: "Fractions"*
ACTIVITY **②** Fraction Flags	🕐 40 MIN 👤 INDIVIDUALS	• *Student Activity Book*, pp. 22–25 • Flag books or posters (optional)
SESSION FOLLOW-UP **③** Daily Practice		• *Student Activity Book*, p. 26 • *Student Math Handbook*, pp. 86, 87, 90

*See *Materials to Prepare,* p. 43.

Classroom Routines

Today's Number: 30 Using Multiples of 5 and 10 and Subtraction Individually students generate expressions for 30 using only subtraction and two numbers that are multiples of 5 and 10. For example: 35 — 5 and 40 — 10.

Flag of Poland

Flag of the Russian Federation

Flag of Mauritius

Parts of a Whole, Parts of a Group

Flags in Halves, Thirds, and Fourths

T75

▲ Transparency, T75 ;

Resource Masters, M13

20 MIN   CLASS

ACTIVITY

1 A Third of a Flag

Display the transparency of Flags in Halves, Thirds, and Fourths (T75) or the chart of these flags that you created in advance.

Here are flags of three different countries. Does anyone recognize any of these flags? What countries are they from?

If students do not recognize any of the flags, tell them what countries they come from. If you have a map of the world, point to where each of the countries is located.

Let's look at the first flag for a moment. This flag is from Poland. The Polish flag is divided into how many parts? (*2*) What part of the Polish flag is [white]? (*one half*)

What about the flag at the bottom, the Mauritius flag? How many parts are in that flag? (*4*) What part of the Mauritius flag is green? (*one fourth*)

Write *half* and $\frac{1}{2}$, *fourth* and $\frac{1}{4}$ on the board.

The middle flag is from Russia. It's divided into three equal parts. Do you know what a piece is called if it's one of three equal parts?

Tell the class that one of three equal parts is called *one third*.

What part of the Russian flag is blue? (*one third*) How do you think we would write *one third*?

Write *one third* and $\frac{1}{3}$ on the board.

When we write fractions, we use two numbers. [Point to the fractions on the board.] Does anyone have an idea about what the bottom number means?

Students may see for themselves that the bottom number matches the number of parts in the whole. They may also say that "$\frac{1}{3}$ stands for 1 out of 3 parts." If students do not see this, point it out to them. You can tell them that the bottom number of a fraction is called the *denominator,* but do not expect students to use this term.

When you write a fraction, the bottom number tells you the number of parts in the whole. For the fraction $\frac{1}{3}$, there are three parts in the whole.

Using students' input, fill in the "Fractions" chart to organize the fractions they know so far. Leave the chart up for students to reference throughout the session. Using this chart, briefly discuss with students that these fractions are in order from the biggest ($\frac{1}{2}$) to smallest ($\frac{1}{4}$). ❶

Fractions

	Number of Equal Pieces	Name of Parts	Fraction
	2	halves	$\frac{1}{2}$
	3	thirds	$\frac{1}{3}$
	4	fourths	$\frac{1}{4}$

Direct students' attention to *Student Activity Book* page 22.

You see the outlines of three flags. Today you're going to color these flags and write what fraction is shown by each color.

Let's do the first flag together. How many parts are in this flag? (*3*) What are the parts called? (*thirds*)❷

The French flag has three parts, so let's color this flag to make it look like France's flag. The first third is blue, so color the first third blue. The next third of France's flag is white, so leave that one white. The last third is red, so color the last third red.

What part of the flag is blue? (*one third*) What part of the flag is white? (*one third*) What part of the flag is red? (*one third*) So next to the flag we can write, "$\frac{1}{3}$ blue, $\frac{1}{3}$ white, $\frac{1}{3}$ red."

Let's look at the second flag. How many parts are in this flag? (2) Are the parts equal? (*yes*) So each part is how much of the flag? (*half*) Color the flag and write the fraction of each color.

Do the same for the last flag on the page. You can pick any colors you like for your flags. When you finish this page, there are three more pages to color, for 12 flags in all.

When students choose the colors of their flags, they need not match any national flag. In this activity, they should color each section of a flag a different color, representing unit fractions (fractions with a numerator of 1). In upcoming sessions, students will work with fractions whose numerators are greater than 1.

Math Note

❶ **Ordering Fractions** Some students will begin to notice that in unit fractions, the greater the number in the denominator, the smaller the fractional piece of a whole.

Teaching Note

❷ **Flags of Many Colors** Flags of many countries are divided into thirds vertically, like the first flag on *Student Activity Book* page 22. Romania's is blue, yellow, red; Senegal's and Mali's are green, yellow, red; Mexico's and Italy's are green, white, red; Ireland's is green, white, orange; and France's is blue, white, red. Pick one to illustrate *Student Activity Book* page 22.

Flag of France

Flag of Mexico

Flag of Mali

Name _____ Date _____

Parts of a Whole, Parts of a Group

Fraction Flags (page 1 of 4)
Color each part of the flag a different color. Then write what fraction of the flag each color is.

Flag 1

Flag 2

Flag 3

22 Unit 7

Session 2.2

▲ **Student Activity Book, p. 22**

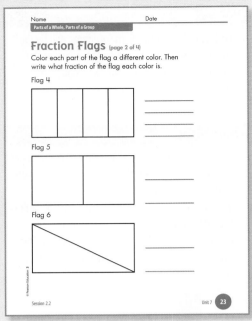

Name ____ Date ____
Parts of a Whole, Parts of a Group

Fraction Flags (page 2 of 4)
Color each part of the flag a different color. Then
write what fraction of the flag each color is.

Flag 4

Flag 5

Flag 6

Session 2.2 Unit 7 23

▲ Student Activity Book, p. 23

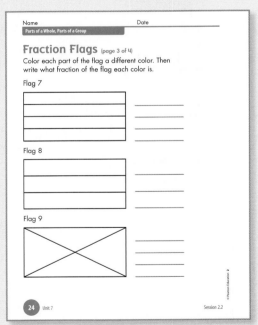

Name ____ Date ____
Parts of a Whole, Parts of a Group

Fraction Flags (page 3 of 4)
Color each part of the flag a different color. Then
write what fraction of the flag each color is.

Flag 7

Flag 8

Flag 9

24 Unit 7 Session 2.2

▲ Student Activity Book, p. 24

ACTIVITY
2 Fraction Flags

40 MIN INDIVIDUALS

Students complete *Student Activity Book* pages 22–25.

*The student colors the flags and writes the fraction
represented by each color.*

ONGOING ASSESSMENT: Observing Students at Work

Students work with halves, thirds, and fourths of a region.

- **Do students label parts of their flags correctly?**

- **Are they able to identify the parts of the their flags with fraction notation?**

DIFFERENTIATION: Supporting the Range of Learners

Extension If some students finish early, they can look through a book, poster, or Web site to find flags that interest them and discuss the fractions each color represents on the chosen flags.

ELL Assess English Language Learners' comprehension of the lesson. Circle the room as they work and check that they shade the correct portions on each flag. Point out and explain errors. Next, on a sheet of paper, write the fractions $\frac{1}{2}$, $\frac{1}{3}$, and $\frac{1}{4}$. Point to $\frac{1}{3}$, and ask:

How do you say this?

Confirm the correct response, and continue with the remaining fractions. Finally, say:

Show me one third.

Have the student point to the numerical fraction on your sheet of paper, and confirm the correct response. If students need further instruction, use a different example. Draw three circles, rather than a flag, and color one of them. Say:

One of the three is colored, so that is $\frac{1}{3}$.

SESSION FOLLOW-UP

3 Daily Practice

 Daily Practice: For ongoing review, have students complete *Student Activity Book* page 26.

 Student Math Handbook: Students and families may use *Student Math Handbook* pages 86, 87, 90 for reference and review. See pages 92–94 in the back of this unit.

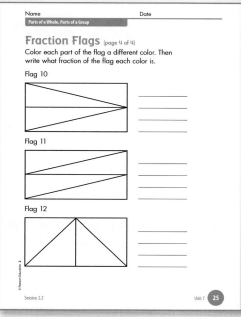

▲ Student Activity Book, p. 25

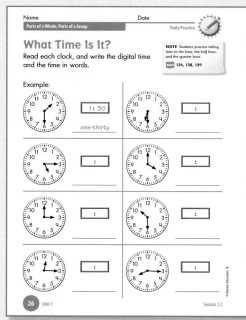

▲ Student Activity Book, p. 26

More Fraction Flags

Math Focus Points

◆ Learning the terms and notation for fractions that contain more than one part (e.g., $\frac{2}{3}$, $\frac{2}{4}$, and $\frac{3}{4}$)

◆ Identifying halves, thirds, and fourths of regions

◆ Identifying and naming fractional parts that have numerators greater than 1 (e.g., $\frac{2}{3}$, $\frac{2}{4}$, $\frac{3}{4}$)

Vocabulary

thirds
two thirds

Today's Plan		Materials
① DISCUSSION **Other Fractions**	🕐 20 MIN 👥 CLASS	• T76* 💻 • Chart: "Thirds and Fourths"*; chart: "Fractions" (from Session 2.2)
② ACTIVITY **Fraction Flags**	🕐 40 MIN 🧍 INDIVIDUALS 👥 GROUPS	• Student Activity Book, pp. 27–30 • Crayons
③ SESSION FOLLOW-UP **Daily Practice and Homework**		• Student Activity Book, pp. 27–31 • Student Math Handbook, pp. 86, 87, 88, 89, 90, 91

*See Materials to Prepare, p. 43.

Classroom Routines

What Time Is It? Post the following times on the board: 2:15, 2:30, and 2:45.

Students work with a partner to practice setting their individual clocks to 15, 30, and 45 minutes past the hour. Then, students take turns writing a time in digital format (3:15) on a piece of paper and setting the clock to that time.

DISCUSSION
Other Fractions

20 MIN   CLASS

Math Focus Points for Discussion

◆ Learning the terms and notation for fractions that contain more than one part (e.g., $\frac{2}{3}$, $\frac{2}{4}$, and $\frac{3}{4}$)

Up until now in this unit, students have worked with unit fractions (fractions with a numerator equal to 1), or fractions that contain one part of a whole (e.g., $\frac{1}{2}$, $\frac{1}{4}$, $\frac{1}{12}$). In this discussion, students are introduced to non-unit fractions (fractions with a numerator greater than 1) that contain more than one part of a whole (e.g., $\frac{3}{5}$, $\frac{2}{4}$, $\frac{2}{3}$).

Using the transparency of Flags in Thirds and Fourths (T76) or the chart of these flags that you created in advance, show the class the first flag and keep the other two hidden.

Flag of Nigeria

This is a picture of the Nigerian flag. What can you tell me about it?

Listen for comments that reflect students' understanding of fractions.

Students might say:

"It's divided into thirds."

"One third is white."

If students do not bring this up, draw their attention to fractions.

This flag is divided into how many equal parts? (*three*) What are the parts called? (*thirds*) How many parts are colored white? (*one*) What fraction of this flag is colored white? (*one third*) If one third of the flag is white, what part of the flag is green?

Parts of a Whole, Parts of a Group
Flags in Thirds and Fourths

T76

▲ Transparencies, T76

❶ **Fractional Parts** A common misunderstanding that some students have when they are first working with non-unit fractions of an area is that the fractional parts must be adjacent to each other. Students will encounter this as they begin to work with equivalent fractions.

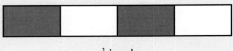

$\frac{1}{2}$ is red
$\frac{2}{4}$ is red

❷ **Fraction Notation** In a fraction, the bottom number represents the number of equal parts in the whole. It is called the denominator. The top number designates the parts of the whole being used. It is called the numerator.

This is the first time in the unit that students have been introduced to fractions made up of more than one part.

Two of the thirds are colored green, so we say that **two thirds** of the flag is green.

Add a row to the "Fractions" chart (from Session 2.2) for $\frac{2}{3}$. Draw a picture of $\frac{2}{3}$ in the first column. Then ask the class how to fill in the columns labeled "Number of Equal Pieces," "Name of Parts," and "Fraction."

Point out to students that in this example, even though the two green thirds are not adjacent, two of the three parts are green. This makes the flag $\frac{2}{3}$ green and $\frac{1}{3}$ white.❶

Fractions

	Number of Equal Pieces	Name of Parts	Fraction
	2	halves	$\frac{1}{2}$
	3	thirds	$\frac{1}{3}$
	4	fourths	$\frac{1}{4}$
	3	thirds	$\frac{2}{3}$

When we write $\frac{2}{3}$, what do you think the 2 stands for and what does the 3 stand for?

Listen to the ways in which students verbalize their ideas. Then confirm that 3 stands for the number of parts in the flag and that 2 stands for the number of parts that are colored green.

You can use the words *denominator* and *numerator* to refer to the parts of the fraction, but do not expect students to use these terms.❷

Next to the flag, write "$\frac{1}{3}$ white, $\frac{2}{3}$ green."

Now show the second flag on the transparency or chart (yellow, blue, and red flag).

Flag of Colombia

This is a picture of the flag of Colombia. What do you notice about this flag?

If students do not comment on how the flag is divided, ask them to use a fraction.

Who can use fractions to describe this flag?

Although there are 3 colors, the flag is divided into 4 regions: 1 colored red, 1 colored blue, and 2 colored yellow. If students suggest that the flag is divided into thirds, emphasize that *thirds* means "3 equal parts." This flag is divided into 4 equal parts, so it is divided into fourths.

What fraction of the flag is red? (*one fourth*) What fraction is blue? (*one fourth*) What fraction is yellow? (*two fourths*)

If students identify the yellow region either as $\frac{2}{4}$ or $\frac{1}{2}$, have them explain why they think it would be called that. Emphasize that $\frac{2}{4}$ means "2 out of 4 equal parts."

If no one addresses the idea that half the flag is yellow, do not bring it up. However, if students suggest that one half of the flag is yellow, have them explain how they know. Can they explain that the part that is yellow is equal to the part that is not yellow? Confirm that $\frac{1}{2}$ and $\frac{2}{4}$ are names for the same amount.

Fill in a row for $\frac{2}{4}$ on the "Fractions" chart (from Session 2.2). Again, ask students to explain what the 4 stands for and what the 2 stands for.

Next to the flag, write "$\frac{1}{4}$ red, $\frac{1}{4}$ blue, $\frac{2}{4}$ yellow."

Now show the third flag.

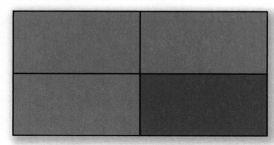

Let's look at one more flag. This is a flag that a country designed. How many colors are on this flag? (*two*) If there are two colors, does that mean that it's divided in half?

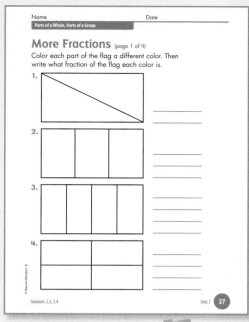

▲ Student Activity Book, p. 27

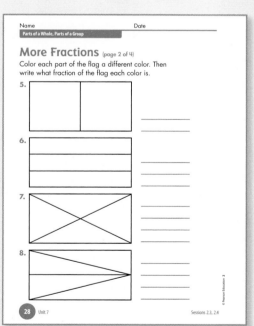

▲ Student Activity Book, p. 28

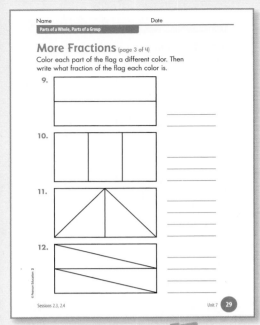

▲ Student Activity Book, p. 29 PORTFOLIO

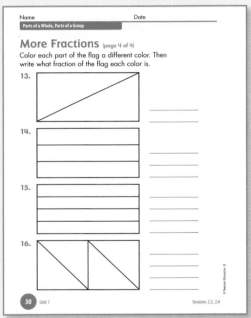

▲ Student Activity Book, p. 30 PORTFOLIO

Have students explain that the flag is not divided in half because the two parts are not equal.

How many equal parts does this flag have? *(four)* What fraction of the flag is blue? ($\frac{1}{4}$) What fraction of the flag is green ($\frac{3}{4}$)?

Use this flag to show students how to write *three fourths* and $\frac{3}{4}$. Fill in a row on the "Fractions" chart (from Session 2.2) for $\frac{3}{4}$. Again, have students explain what the 4 stands for and what the 3 stands for.

Next to the blue and green flag, write "$\frac{1}{4}$ blue, $\frac{3}{4}$ green."

ACTIVITY

② Fraction Flags

40 MIN   INDIVIDUALS   GROUPS

Student Activity Book pages 27–30 each contain four flag outlines divided into halves, thirds, or fourths. Organize the class in four groups and have each group start on a different page. This arrangement will foster the completion of a wider variety of flags in a shorter period of time.

You are going to make up your own flags on *Student Activity Book* pages 27–30. As you color your flags, I want you to think about different kinds of fractions. For example, if your flag is divided into fourths, you might choose to color $\frac{3}{4}$ one color and $\frac{1}{4}$ another, or $\frac{2}{4}$ and $\frac{1}{4}$ and $\frac{1}{4}$, or $\frac{2}{4}$ and $\frac{2}{4}$. When you finish coloring your flag, write what fraction of the flag is shown by each color.

Students design their own flags as they explore fractional relationships.

ONGOING ASSESSMENT: Observing Students at Work

As students design and color their flags, they are working with halves, thirds, and fourths.

- **Are students able to identify whether flags are divided into halves, thirds, or fourths?**

- **Can students name and write fractions that have more than one part?**

DIFFERENTIATION: Supporting the Range of Learners

 If students are having difficulty with unit fractions (fractions with a numerator of 1), encourage them to make each section of the flag a different color. Otherwise, have students color their flags to illustrate non-unit fractions (fractions with numerators larger than 1).

SESSION FOLLOW-UP

3 Daily Practice and Homework

 Daily Practice: For ongoing review, have students complete *Student Activity Book* page 31.

 Homework: Students finish coloring and labeling their fraction flags on *Student Activity Book* pages 27–30.

 Student Math Handbook: Students and families may use *Student Math Handbook* pages 86, 87, 88, 89, 90, 91 for reference and review. See pages 92–94 in the back of this unit.

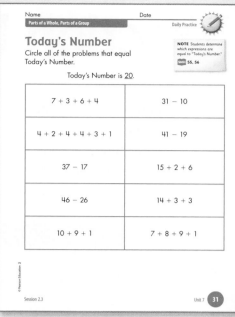

Today's Number
Circle all of the problems that equal Today's Number.

NOTE Students determine which expressions are equal to "Today's Number."

Today's Number is 20.

7 + 3 + 6 + 4	31 − 10
4 + 2 + 4 + 4 + 3 + 1	41 − 19
37 − 17	15 + 2 + 6
46 − 26	14 + 3 + 3
10 + 9 + 1	7 + 8 + 9 + 1

▲ **Student Activity Book, p. 31**

Fraction Flag Posters

Math Focus Points

◆ Identifying and naming fractional parts that have numerators greater than 1 (e.g., $\frac{2}{3}$, $\frac{2}{4}$, $\frac{3}{4}$)

◆ Learning the terms and notation for fractions that contain more than one part (e.g., $\frac{2}{3}$, $\frac{2}{4}$, and $\frac{3}{4}$)

◆ Identifying halves, thirds, and fourths of regions.

Today's Plan		Materials
ACTIVITY **① Creating Fraction Flag Posters**	35 MIN INDIVIDUALS	• *Student Activity Book*, pp. 27–30 (from Session 2.3) • M15–M22* • Fraction Flag Charts*; crayons; tape
DISCUSSION **② Looking at Our Fraction Flag Posters**	25 MIN CLASS	• "Fraction Flags" posters (from Activity 1)
SESSION FOLLOW-UP **③ Daily Practice**		• *Student Activity Book*, p. 32 • *Student Math Handbook*, pp. 86, 87, 88, 89, 90, 91

*See *Materials to Prepare*, p. 43.

Classroom Routines

Quick Images: Tens and Ones Show Image 1 from *Quick Images 3: Tens and Ones*, T74. Follow the basic *Quick Images* activity. Ask students to determine the total number of squares. Record the equations $40 + 3 = 43$ and $50 - 7 = 43$. Repeat for Images 2 and 3.

ACTIVITY

① Creating Fraction Flag Posters

35 MIN   INDIVIDUALS

Show students the posters in the room labeled with fractions represented by different flags, such as "$\frac{3}{4}$ and $\frac{1}{4}$," "$\frac{2}{4}$ and $\frac{1}{4}$ and $\frac{1}{4}$," "$\frac{2}{3}$ and $\frac{1}{3}$." Explain that each student will select one of the flags he or she made on *Student Activity Book* pages 27–30 and duplicate it onto the templates of Fraction Flags (M15–M22). ① Check to make sure that students have correctly identified the fractions illustrated by their flags.

Students tape their Fraction Flags onto the appropriate posters.

Encourage students to pick different flags so that each poster has a variety. You may suggest that some students make more than one so that every poster has at least a few examples.

ONGOING ASSESSMENT: Observing Students at Work

- **Have students correctly identified the fraction represented by each color of their flag?**

DIFFERENTIATION: Supporting the Range of Learners

Intervention If students are having difficulty with unit fractions (fractions with a numerator of 1), encourage them to select a flag in which each section is a different color and post it on the "$\frac{1}{2}$ and $\frac{1}{2}$," "$\frac{1}{3}$ and $\frac{1}{3}$ and $\frac{1}{3}$," or "$\frac{1}{4}$ and $\frac{1}{4}$ and $\frac{1}{4}$ and $\frac{1}{4}$" posters. Otherwise, have students choose flags to illustrate non-unit fractions (fractions with a numerator larger than 1).

Teaching Note

① **Fraction Flag Templates** Template flags from Fraction Flags (M15–M22) are numbered to correspond to the flags on *Student Activity Book* pages 27–30.

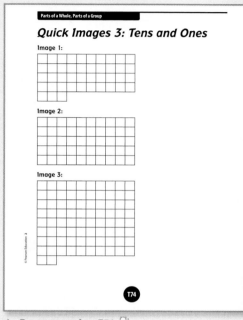

Parts of a Whole, Parts of a Group

Quick Images 3: Tens and Ones

Image 1:

Image 2:

Image 3:

T74

▲ Transparencies, T74

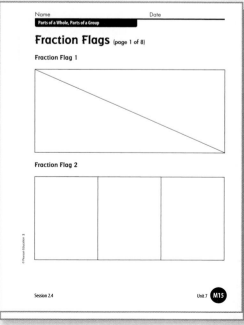

Name _____   Date _____

Parts of a Whole, Parts of a Group

Fraction Flags (page 1 of 8)

Fraction Flag 1

Fraction Flag 2

Session 2.4   Unit 7 M15

▲ Resource Masters, M15–M16

Professional Development

② **Dialogue Box:** Talking About Fraction Flags, p. 87

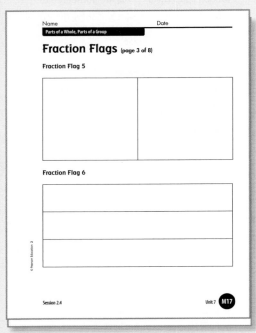

▲ Resource Masters, M17–M18

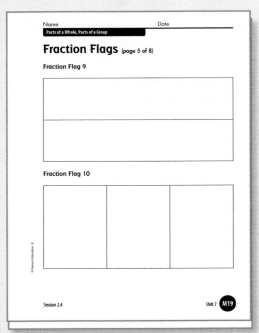

▲ Resource Masters, M19–M20

Extension Students who work quickly and correctly should be encouraged to color flags from additional templates to add to the "Fraction Flag" posters that have only a few examples.

DISCUSSION

② Looking at Our Fraction Flag Posters

25 MIN   CLASS

Math Focus Points for Discussion

◆ Identifying halves, thirds, and fourths of regions

◆ Learning the terms and notation for fractions that contain more than one part (e.g., $\frac{2}{3}$, $\frac{2}{4}$, and $\frac{3}{4}$)

For the last few days, we've been making Fraction Flags to learn about halves, thirds, and fourths and to see different ways to make those fractions. Take a look at our Fraction Flag posters. What do you notice when you look at them?②

Do you think all of the flags have been placed on the correct posters? Do you have any questions about why a flag was put where it was?

Students may find an incorrectly placed flag or may have a question about why a particular flag appears on a given poster. Ask them to identify and discuss those in question and, if necessary, help relocate an incorrectly placed flag.

Point to the poster labeled "$\frac{1}{3}$ and $\frac{1}{3}$ and $\frac{1}{3}$."

Look at all the flags on this poster that show $\frac{1}{3}$ and $\frac{1}{3}$ and $\frac{1}{3}$. Why do all of these flags belong on this poster?

Students might say:

"All the flags are divided into three equal parts and each part is a different color."

Point to the poster labeled "$\frac{2}{3}$ and $\frac{1}{3}$."

Look at all the flags on this poster that show $\frac{2}{3}$ and $\frac{1}{3}$. Why do all of these flags belong on this poster?

Students might say:

"All the parts are the same size. Two parts are one color and the other part is another color."

If the flag has two colors and is divided into two parts, why isn't it on the $\frac{1}{2}$ and $\frac{1}{2}$ poster?

Students might say:

"The two parts are not equal, so they aren't halves."

Point to one flag on the poster labeled "$\frac{1}{3}$ and $\frac{1}{3}$ and $\frac{1}{3}$."

Explain to me why this flag belongs here and why it doesn't go with the $\frac{2}{3}$ and $\frac{1}{3}$ poster.

Continue with similar questions about the different posters that show fourths.

SESSION FOLLOW-UP

Daily Practice

 Daily Practice: For reinforcement of this unit's content, have students complete *Student Activity Book* page 32.

Student Math Handbook: Students and families may use *Student Math Handbook* pages 86, 87, 88, 89, 90, 91 for reference and review. See pages 92–94 in the back of this unit.

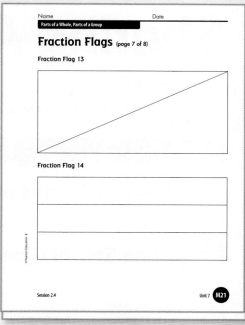

▲ Resource Masters, M21–M22

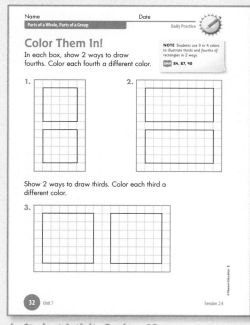

▲ Student Activity Book, p. 32

Sharing Among Friends

Math Focus Points
◆ Finding thirds and fourths of sets

Today's Plan		Materials
① DISCUSSION **Thirds and Fourths of Sets**	15 MIN PAIRS CLASS	• Connecting cubes (35 per pair)
② ACTIVITY **Sharing Sets of Objects**	45 MIN PAIRS	• *Student Activity Book*, pp. 33–35 (p. 35 is optional) • Connecting cubes
③ SESSION FOLLOW-UP **Daily Practice**		• *Student Activity Book*, p. 36 • *Student Math Handbook*, pp. 87, 90

Classroom Routines

Today's Number: 15 with Missing Parts Each student completes *Today's Number* (M23). Use T77 and select a couple examples for students to discuss how they solved the problem. This work will give you some information on how students are understanding and working with Today's Number. In addition, this is the seventh in a series of work samples for Today's Number that will be collected throughout the year.

DISCUSSION

1 Thirds and Fourths of Sets

15 MIN   PAIRS   CLASS

Math Focus Points for Discussion

◆ Finding thirds and fourths of sets

Up until this activity, students have found thirds and fourths of regions. In this activity, they find thirds and fourths of sets. Distribute about 35 cubes per pair.

Remind the class about Linda and Ebony, the twins who share everything. Today, their friend Kira is playing with them, so the girls must share everything three ways.

Linda, Ebony, and Kira have a jar with buttons in it. If they share a bunch of buttons, what fraction does each girl get?

Before asking for an answer, have students close their eyes and picture a jar of buttons and the 3 girls who are going to share them. Emphasize that the girls need to divide the buttons into 3 equal shares.

Because all of the previous sharing problems involved only 2 girls, some students may say that each girl gets half of the buttons. If this happens, let other students point out that because there are 3 girls, splitting the buttons in half would mean that 1 girl would be left out. To share among 3 girls, each girl must get one third of the buttons.❶

The 3 girls have 12 buttons to share. How many buttons would each girl get? Use your cubes to show what is happening in this problem and how many buttons each girl will get.

Professional Development

❶ **Dialogue Box:** Thirds and Fourths of Sets, p. 89

Name _____   Date _____

Parts of a Whole, Parts of a Group

Today's Number
Today's Number is 15.

$40 - \underline{\quad} = 15$	$35 - \underline{\quad} = 15$
$60 - \underline{\quad} = 15$	$\underline{\quad} - 5 = 15$
$55 - \underline{\quad} = 15$	$100 - \underline{\quad} = 15$
$\underline{\quad} - 0 = 15$	$20 - \underline{\quad} = 15$
$50 - \underline{\quad} = 15$	$\underline{\quad} - 15 = 15$

Session 2.5   Unit 7 M23

▲ **Resource Masters, M23; T77** PORTFOLIO

Students use cubes to solve the problem. They divide 12 cubes into 3 groups to determine that each person gets 4 buttons.

Have one or two students explain how they solved the problem. Make sure that at least one student models the problem with cubes. If there is disagreement, have students present their thinking and use this as an opportunity to clarify what the problem is about. When 4 is established as the answer to the problem, go back to the question.

How many buttons are there in all? (*12*) What fraction does each girl get? (*one third*) How many buttons does each girl get? (*4*) Each girl gets $\frac{1}{3}$ of the 12 buttons, so each girl gets 4 buttons.

Now do a problem involving fourths.

Jake, Bob, Tim, and David are playing together. They have 8 buttons to share equally. What fraction of the buttons will each boy get?

Go through the same visualization exercise as above before asking students to name the fraction each boy gets. (*one fourth*)

How many boys are sharing the buttons? (*4*) How many buttons does each boy get? (*2*) What is one fourth of 8? (*2*)

Most students should see that each boy gets 2 buttons. Have several students explain how they solved the problems. Make sure that at least one student models the problem with cubes. Use the following language:

One fourth of 8 buttons is 2 buttons. Each boy gets $\frac{1}{4}$ of the 8 buttons, so each boy gets 2 buttons.

ACTIVITY
② Sharing Sets of Objects

45 MIN   PAIRS

Have students complete *Student Activity Book* pages 33–34, in which three or four friends share sets of objects equally; that is, the sets are divided into thirds or fourths. The problems on these pages all have whole-number answers.

ONGOING ASSESSMENT: Observing Students at Work ✓

Students find thirds and fourths of sets of objects.

- **How do students find $\frac{1}{3}$ or $\frac{1}{4}$ of a set?** Do they count out objects and then distribute them into 3 or 4 groups? Do they use numerical reasoning?

- **If students work on *Student Activity Book* page 35, are they able to solve the problems by using mixed numbers?**

DIFFERENTIATION: Supporting the Range of Learners

Intervention If students have difficulty interpreting the action of the problem, have them write the names of the children on separate sheets of paper. Then, have students count out the number of objects to be shared and arrange each child's share on the paper.

Students determine each child's share by distributing the cubes on separate sheets of paper.

Name _____ Date _____

Parts of a Whole, Parts of a Group

Friends at Play (page 1 of 2)

Linda, Ebony, and Kira are playing together.

1. Kira's mother gave them 24 peanuts. Each girl gets one third of the peanuts.
   How many peanuts does each girl get? _____

   How did you figure it out?

2. The girls have 15 stickers. Each girl gets one third of the stickers.
   How many stickers does each girl get? _____

   How did you figure it out?

3. The girls play a game with 30 cards. Each girl gets one third of the cards.
   How many cards does each girl get? _____

   How did you figure it out?

Sessions 2.5, 2.6   Unit 7 **33**

▲ **Student Activity Book, p. 33**

Name _____ Date _____

Parts of a Whole, Parts of a Group

Friends at Play (page 2 of 2)

Jake, Bob, Tim, and David are playing together.

4. Jake's mother gave them 32 peanuts. Each boy gets one fourth of the peanuts.
   How many peanuts does each boy get? _____

   How did you figure it out?

5. The boys have 24 stickers. Each boy gets one fourth of the stickers.
   How many stickers does each boy get? _____

   How did you figure it out?

6. The boys are playing a game with 28 cards. Each boy gets one fourth of the cards.
   How many cards does each boy get? _____

   How did you figure it out?

34 Unit 7   Sessions 2.5, 2.6

▲ **Student Activity Book, p. 34**

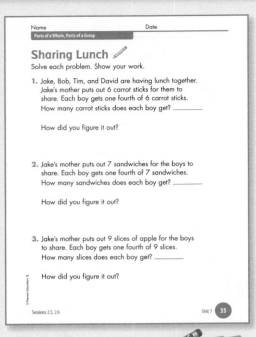

▲ Student Activity Book, p. 35

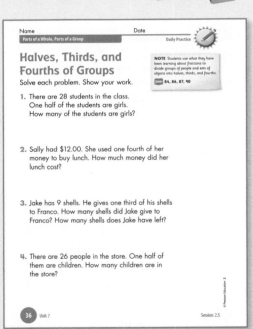

▲ Student Activity Book, p. 36

Extension If students are confident about their solutions to the problems on *Student Activity Book* pages 33–34, allow them to begin working on *Student Activity Book* page 35, which involves mixed numbers (for example, $1\frac{1}{2}$).

ELL As you present the examples, draw sketches on the board to help English Language Learners follow the significant details in the problem. For example, draw three stick figures, and label them Linda, Ebony, and Kira. Sketch a jar, and draw 12 circles inside the jar to represent buttons. Then write the questions students are to answer beneath the sketches.

SESSION FOLLOW-UP
③ Daily Practice

Daily Practice: For reinforcement of today's session, have students complete *Student Activity Book* page 36.

Student Math Handbook: Students and families may use *Student Math Handbook* pages 87, 90 for reference and review. See pages 92–94 in the back of this unit.

End-of-Unit Assessment

Math Focus Points

◆ Identifying halves, thirds, and fourths of a region

◆ Finding fractions of sets

Today's Plan		Materials
① ASSESSMENT ACTIVITY **End-of-Unit Assessment** ✓ 🕐 👤 40 MIN INDIVIDUALS		• *Student Activity Book*, pp. 33–35 (from Session 2.5) • M24–M25*
② DISCUSSION **Fractions Wrap-up** 🕐 👥 20 MIN CLASS		• Chart: "What We Know About $\frac{1}{2}$" (from Session 1.1)
③ SESSION FOLLOW-UP **Daily Practice**		• *Student Activity Book*, p. 37 • *Student Math Handbook*, pp. 84, 86–88, 90

*See *Materials to Prepare*, p. 45.

Classroom Routines

What Time Is It? Post the following times on the board: 5:15, 5:30, and 5:45.

Students work with a partner to practice setting their individual clocks to 15, 30, and 45 minutes past the hour. Then, students take turns writing a time in digital format (3:15) on a sheet of paper and setting the clock to that time.

Teaching Note

1 Extra Support Make sure that all students have whatever support they need to understand the format and directions of the assessment so that you get a fair reading of the students' performance on the mathematics problems. This may include reading directions to students.

Professional Development

2 Teacher Note: End-of-Unit Assessment, p. 79

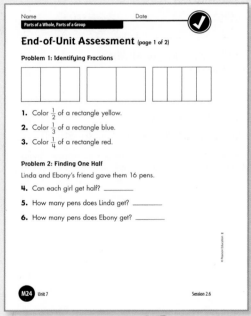

▲ **Resource Masters, M24** PORTFOLIO

ASSESSMENT ACTIVITY

End-of-Unit Assessment Problems

40 MIN   INDIVIDUALS

Let students know that today they are going to work on some problems about fractions individually. Each of the three problems on End-of-Unit-Assessment (M24–M25) is a different kind of problem related to the work students have done in the unit. Students can work on the three problems in any order.

Problem 1 has students find fractional parts of a whole and addresses Benchmark 1: Identify $\frac{1}{2}$, $\frac{1}{3}$, $\frac{1}{4}$ of a region. Problem 2 asks students to find one half of a set and addresses Benchmark 2: Find $\frac{1}{2}$ of a set of objects. In Problem 3, students select a representation of thirds. This problem addresses Benchmark 3: Recognize that a fraction divides the whole into equal parts.

Make sure that students understand the directions for each problem. The purpose of the assessment is to see how students work with the math ideas of this unit, so provide whatever support is needed to read and understand the directions.**1**

Problems 1 and 2 are fairly straightforward. Problem 3 asks students to consider different students' perspectives and to write about whether they agree or disagree with the students. It may be necessary to read through this question with the class or with individual students to make sure that they understand the format and understand what they are supposed to do. Make sure that students are writing enough for you to understand their thinking. Encourage students to reread their answers to make sure that their responses are clear. Consider asking students to clarify their answers if their thinking is not clear. Make note of any questions or prompts you gave to students so that you can consider this as you read their responses.

Do as much observation and note-taking as you can while students are engaged in the assessment. The paper-and-pencil task will provide some information, but you will gain additional information by observing students' work.**2**

It is likely that the assessment will not take students more than 40 minutes. As students finish the assessment problems, they can continue to work on *Student Activity Book* pages 33–35 from the previous session. Plan to spend the final 20 minutes with an ending discussion about the fraction work in this unit.

DISCUSSION
② Fractions Wrap-up

20 MIN   CLASS

Math Focus Points for Discussion

◆ Sharing what is known about fractions

We have been thinking about fractions for two weeks. What do you now know about fractions?

Encourage students to think about the activities they worked on and to look around the room at the fraction charts and the Fraction Flag posters before sharing their ideas.

Students may talk about the sort of activities they did, such as solving story problems that involved sharing, folding paper into fractions, and making Fraction Flags. Encourage them to think beyond the activities and focus them on the math ideas involved.

When you were making Fraction Flags, what did you have to know about fractions or what were you learning about fractions that helped you work on that activity?

As students share, listen for ideas that indicate their understanding of the benchmarks for this unit, such as a fractions' being about equal parts of a set or a region. Some students may talk about the following:

- The way fractions are written and what that notation means, noting the role of the bottom number (denominator) and the top number (numerator)

- Fractional numbers that are new to them

Some students may raise ideas that go beyond the benchmarks for this unit. For example, they may mention the following:

- Sixths or eighths

- Fractions such as $\frac{4}{4}$ or $\frac{8}{4}$

- The fact that the larger the bottom number, the smaller the piece

At some point during the discussion refer students back to the poster "What We Know About $\frac{1}{2}$" that was created in the Session 1.1 of the unit.

At the beginning of our work, we had a discussion about one half. Here are some of the things you said. What do you now know about one half that we should add to our poster?

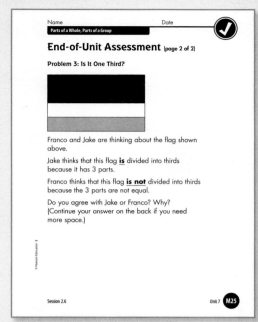

▲ Resource Masters, M25 *PORTFOLIO*

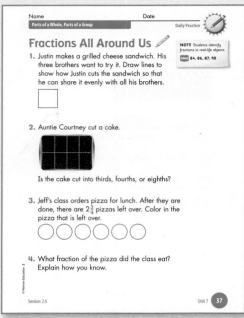

▲ Student Activity Book, p. 37

Students might say:

"Half means two equal parts or pieces."

"You can find half of one thing or half of a set of things."

"If you take half of an odd number you end up with the fraction $\frac{1}{2}$ in your answer."

 SESSION FOLLOW-UP
Daily Practice

 Daily Practice: For enrichment, have students complete *Student Activity Book* page 37.

Student Math Handbook: Students and families may use *Student Math Handbook* pages 84, 86–88, 90 for reference and review. See pages 92–94 in the back of this unit.

Professional Development

UNIT 7

Parts of a Whole, Parts of a Group

Teacher Notes

In Part 6 of *Implementing Investigations in Grade 2,* you will find a set of Teacher Notes that addresses topics and issues applicable to the curriculum as a whole rather than to specific curriculum units. They include the following:

Computational Fluency and Place Value

Computational Algorithms and Methods

Representations and Contexts for Mathematical Work

Foundations of Algebra in the Elementary Grades

Discussing Mathematical Ideas

Racial and Linguistic Diversity in the Classroom:
    What Does Equity Mean in Today's Math Classroom?

Dialogue Boxes

Teacher Note

Learning About Fractions

Many students come to this unit with an understanding that *half* indicates a *part* of an object or set. However, as the word *half* is used in common language, it does not necessarily imply the precision of the mathematical definition. The new idea for many students is that half indicates two *equal* parts.

One half is an example of a new kind of number—the fraction—and this new kind of number brings with it new conceptual challenges. Up until now, numbers have been associated with the action of counting to designate quantity. Fractions fall *in between* the counting numbers.

A fractional quantity is designated by *two* counting numbers in relation to each other and in relation to a given whole. For example, the quantity $\frac{3}{4}$ *of a rectangle* is designated by the two counting numbers 3 and 4, in relation to each other and in relation to one whole rectangle. The denominator (the bottom number of the fraction) indicates the number of equal parts that make up the whole; the numerator (the top number of the fraction) indicates the number of those parts that make up the quantity. In the figure below, $\frac{3}{4}$ of the rectangle is shaded. The whole is divided into four equal parts (the denominator), and three of these parts (the numerator) make up the shaded quantity.

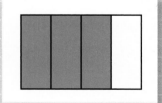

In this example, the whole (the rectangle) is a single object. However, the whole can also be a set of objects. The example of $\frac{3}{4}$ of a bag of 8 marbles is shown below.

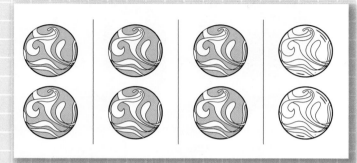

As students move beyond $\frac{1}{2}$ to consider other fractional amounts, they must keep in mind that fractions always involve *equal* parts. Throughout the unit, look for opportunities to pose questions to students that draw their attention to this idea.

In this unit, students work with unit fractions, or fractions such as $\frac{1}{2}$, $\frac{1}{3}$, and $\frac{1}{4}$ that have a numerator of 1. They also work with fractions whose numerator is greater than 1, such as $\frac{2}{3}$, $\frac{2}{4}$, and $\frac{3}{4}$. As students engage in the activities, they may begin to think about other types of fractions. For example, some students may realize that $\frac{4}{4}$ is a whole that is expressed as a fraction.

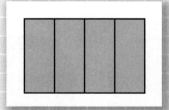

Some students may also realize that fractions can represent quantities greater than 1. For example, if two sandwiches are cut in half and one person takes three pieces, that person has three half sandwiches, or $\frac{3}{2}$ of a sandwich.

Students may also notice that different fractions can represent the same quantity. For example, $\frac{2}{4}$ of a sandwich is the same as $\frac{1}{2}$ of a sandwich.

$\frac{4}{4}$ of a sandwich is the same as 1 whole sandwich.

$\frac{3}{2}$ of a sandwich is the same as $1\frac{1}{2}$ sandwiches.

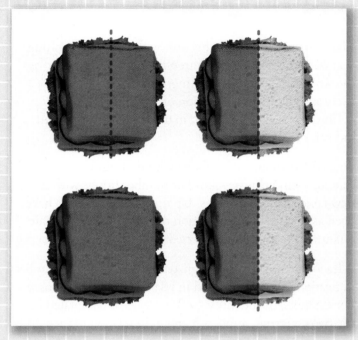

Students continue to develop their knowledge and understanding about fractions as they work with fractions of a single whole and fractions of a set of objects in later grades.

End-of-Unit Assessment

Problem 1

In this problem, students identify and color fractions of rectangles.

Benchmark addressed:

Benchmark 1: Identify $\frac{1}{2}$, $\frac{1}{3}$, and $\frac{1}{4}$ of a region.

In order to meet the benchmark, students' work should show that they can:

• Color 1 of the 3 regions of the first rectangle blue;

• Color 1 of the 2 regions of the second rectangle yellow or color 2 of the 4 regions in the third rectangle yellow;

• Color 1 of the 4 regions of the third rectangle red.

A student may color 2 of the 4 regions of the third rectangle yellow, demonstrating understanding that $\frac{2}{4}$ is equivalent to $\frac{1}{2}$.

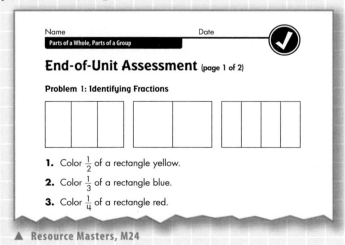

Name		Date	✓

Parts of a Whole, Parts of a Group

End-of-Unit Assessment (page 1 of 2)

Problem 1: Identifying Fractions

1. Color $\frac{1}{2}$ of a rectangle yellow.
2. Color $\frac{1}{3}$ of a rectangle blue.
3. Color $\frac{1}{4}$ of a rectangle red.

▲ **Resource Masters, M24**

Meeting the Benchmark

At the end of this unit, most second graders will fill in the rectangles as Leo does.

Note that Anita chose to color $\frac{2}{4}$ of the third rectangle yellow indicating that she sees $\frac{2}{4}$ as another way of showing $\frac{1}{2}$.

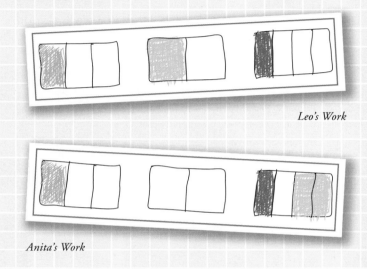

Leo's Work

Anita's Work

Partially Meeting the Benchmark

Students who partially meet the benchmark may identify and color one of the fractional parts incorrectly, or they may identify only two of the three fractions. It is important to ask these students to double-check their work and to explain their work to you.

Not Meeting the Benchmark

Some students may not yet understand that $\frac{1}{2}$ is 1 of 2 equal parts, $\frac{1}{3}$ is 1 of 3 equal parts, and $\frac{1}{4}$ is 1 of 4 equal parts. Students who color the entire first rectangle blue, all of the second rectangle yellow, and the entire third rectangle red do not meet the benchmark. However, their work may indicate that they associate $\frac{1}{2}$ with a whole divided into 2 parts, $\frac{1}{3}$ with a whole divided into 3 parts, and $\frac{1}{4}$ with a whole divided into 4 parts.

Problem 2

In this problem, students find $\frac{1}{2}$ of a set of objects.

Benchmark addressed:

Benchmark 2: Find $\frac{1}{2}$ of a set of objects.

In order to meet the benchmark, students' work should show that they can:

- Find $\frac{1}{2}$ of a set.

Problem 2: Finding One Half

Linda and Ebony's friend gave them 16 pens.

4. Can each girl get half? _____

5. How many pens does Linda get? _____

6. How many pens does Ebony get? _____

© Pearson Education 2

M24 Unit 7   Session 2.6

▲ **Resource Masters, M24**

Meeting the Benchmark

Students who meet the benchmark will recognize that each girl can get half and will find that each girl gets 8 pens. At the end of this unit, almost all second graders will answer these questions correctly: "Yes, each girl can get half, and each girl gets 8 pens."

Some students know that $8 + 8 = 16$ and can use their knowledge of this combination to solve the problem. Other students may draw tally marks and divide them into two equal groups.

Partially Meeting the Benchmark

Some students may misinterpret the problem and may need help focusing on what the problem requires. For example, a student might start out by trying to share the 16 pens among three girls, perhaps because the class worked on a similar problem toward the end of the unit. You might point out that only two girls share the pens in this problem.

If the student is able to solve the problem correctly after receiving help, give him or her another similar problem to solve.

Not Meeting the Benchmark

Some students may write, "No, the girls cannot get half."

Holly said that one girl would get 7 pens and the other 9. Although Holly found a correct combination of 16, she did not recognize that it is possible for each girl to get half.

Problem 3

In this problem, students look at a Fraction Flag and consider two different perspectives about whether the flag is divided into thirds.

Benchmark addressed:

Benchmark 3: Recognize that a fraction divides the whole into *equal* parts.

In order to meet the benchmark, students' work should show that they can:

- Recognize whether fractional parts are equal.

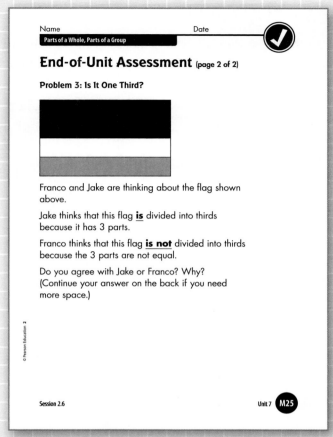

▲ Resource Masters, M25

Meeting the Benchmark

Students who meet the benchmark will agree with Franco and explain that *thirds* means 3 equal parts. The following examples of student work provide a range of typical responses. All of these students meet the benchmark; they agree with Franco. Their responses give some indication of the importance of equal parts.

To support his answer, Simon wrote, "I know Franco is right because there is a big part, and the other parts are smaller."

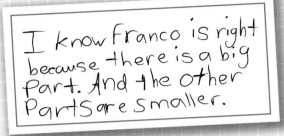

Simon's Work

Chen also agreed with Franco. To support his answer, he drew a flag divided into 2 equal parts to show what $\frac{1}{2}$ looks like and a flag divided into 3 equal parts to show what $\frac{1}{3}$ looks like.

Chen's Work

At times, you may want to ask students to clarify what they have written. For example, Rochelle explained that the darker portion of the flag (which is $\frac{1}{2}$) is bigger (than the other parts). She went on to say that if that part were made into $\frac{2}{4}$, she would agree with Jake.

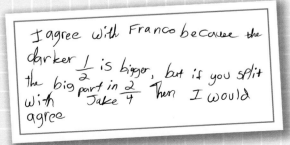

Rochelle's Work

Rochelle sees not only that the three regions are unequal but also that the black region could be divided to make up $\frac{2}{4}$ of the flag. Her teacher may want to ask Rochelle what she meant when she said she would then agree with Jake. For example, does she agree that the flag would be divided into thirds? If so, she would not meet the benchmark. Does she mean that when the black region is split, the flag would be divided into *fourths?* If so, she would meet the benchmark.

Partially Meeting the Benchmark

Students who partially meet the benchmark may agree with Franco and provide relevant explanations, but their writing may contain errors about the meaning of *thirds*. Again, provide these students with an opportunity to express their thinking orally.

For example, Leigh wrote the following:

> I agree with Franko because only two thirds of the rectngle are equal, one of them is not equal.

Leigh's Work

Leigh's reasoning is relevant to the question, but her explanation reveals her misunderstanding. She refers to the white and gray portions of the flag as two *thirds,* when, by agreeing with Franco, she has already said that the flag is not divided into thirds. Her teacher might ask her to explain orally to see what she understands about the white and gray portions of the flag. If Leigh had written that "only 2 *parts* of the rectangle are equal," her response would have been fully correct.

Not Meeting the Benchmark

Students, such as Randall, who do not meet the benchmark will agree with Jake, noting that there are three parts but not yet knowing that thirds divide a whole into 3 *equal* parts.

> I agree with Jake Because if you count them there are 3.

Randall's Work

Some students may agree with Franco but may offer an explanation that is irrelevant to the flag's being divided into thirds. For example, Malcolm wrote the following:

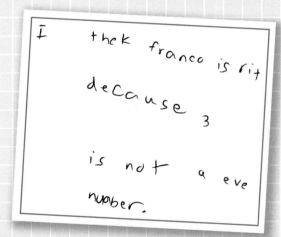

> I thek franco is rit decause 3 is not a eve nuber.

Malcolm's Work

These ideas about fractions are complex for second graders, and some students will need more opportunities to sort them out. In the Grade 2 measurement unit, *Measuring Length and Time,* students will work with fractions again when they measure objects and when they mark timelines in $\frac{1}{2}$- or $\frac{1}{4}$-hour intervals.

Consider having students who do not meet the benchmarks of this unit do more work with Fraction Flags or solve more "Linda and Ebony" problems. Look for opportunities in daily activities to ask questions about one half, one third, and one fourth.

Dialogue Box

What Is One Half?

At the beginning of this unit on fractions, the teacher asks students what they know about one half. Students have many ideas, given their experiences with time, length, shapes, and other fractions that appear in their daily lives. They refer to representations they have used throughout the year, such as the number line and the 100 chart, as well as concepts they have worked on, such as symmetry.

Teacher: Today we are starting a study of fractions. What can you tell me about one half?

Anita: If you cut something down the middle, then it is a half of something.

Tia: Each side of it is a half.

Teacher: Anita, help me think about an example. What could you cut in half?

Anita: A square.

Alberto: And then you'd have 2 rectangles.

Leo: Or 2 triangles.

Teacher: Do you have any other ideas about one half?

Esteban: One day we were playing a game of guess how many fingers I have behind my back and I thought of just putting half my finger behind my back so I didn't have one or zero; I had half. I put half my finger up so only half of it was showing.

Melissa: If you have two of the same thing and you put them together, then you won't have any more halves.

Teacher: Give me an example, Melissa.

Melissa: If you have 2 pieces of a circle and you put them together, you won't have any halves, just a whole circle.

Teacher: Any other ideas about half?

Juan: It's sort of like a clock. It's like 30 minutes.

Teacher: Can you give me the whole idea there? Tell me more about 30 minutes.

Juan: Half an hour and half an hour make an hour.

Teacher: So if you look at the big hand on the clock, start at the 12, and then move halfway around the clock to the 6, that's equal to half an hour. It's also half of the clock, or half of the circle.

Esteban: So that's why they call it half an hour!

Chen: A connection to Juan's idea is that you can also do that on the number line. If you go to 30 on a number line and add another 30 it would be like Juan's.

Teacher: What would 30 on the number line be half of?

Chen: 60.

Henry: If something's whole, like a butterfly, and you cut it right in the middle, it has equal things on both sides. It's symmetrical. And if you put it back together it will make the butterfly.

Gregory: If you cut the 100 chart between the 50 and the 60 you would get 50 and 50 and that would be half of the 100 chart.

Teacher: Does anyone know how we would write *one half* in words or in symbols?

Melissa: You would write a 1 and then a line below and then a 2 at the bottom.

Simon: No, you would do a slash and then a 2.

Chen: Yeah, that's what it looks like on a measuring cup or when you're making a cake.

Jeffrey: You can write it as either.

Teacher: Jeffrey's right; you can write it either way [writes both ways on the chart paper and then writes *one half* in words]. Is *one half* the same as *one and a half*?

Paige: No, because an hour and a half is a whole hour and a half.

Teacher: We've been talking about cutting things. If I do this (rip a piece of paper into 2 pieces approximately $\frac{1}{4}$ and $\frac{3}{4}$ of the original piece of paper), does it make two halves?

Luis: No.

Teacher: Why not, Luis?

Luis: Because one of them is a strip and one of them is a square. They need to be the same size, so they have to be equal.

Teacher: Right, so 2 halves have to be 2 equal parts.

Simon: Like half a mile.

Teacher: Right. It's 1 mile split into 2 equal pieces, and that's why 30 minutes is half an hour. It's 60 minutes split into 2 equal pieces. Do you have to rip things into pieces to get half? Is there another way to get half?

Leigh: There has to be an answer because you're asking us!

Teacher: Imagine that this (a pad of self-stick notes) is a deck of cards. If there are 10 cards here, how would I make half? Would I rip all of the cards?

Melissa: No, you have to have the same amount. So you'd each get 5 cards.

As students in this class offered their ideas about one half, the teacher frequently asked them to elaborate, requesting more detail or a specific example. When Juan introduced 30 minutes as an example of one half, the teacher connected his comments with the ideas the class had been working on in "What Time Is It?". As the discussion continued, the teacher posed questions to find out what students already knew about writing fractions and to introduce the idea of half of a set of discrete objects (half of a deck of cards).

Dialogue Box

Fourths: Same or Different?

During Session 2.1, students in this class folded square pieces of paper into fourths and found three different ways to show fourths. Now they consider whether some fourths represent a larger quantity than others or whether all fourths are the same size.

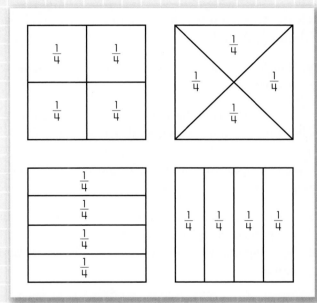

Teacher: I have a question for you. Let's say that these pieces of paper are sandwiches and we cut them in different ways. If I gave you a piece from this sandwich [pointing to the first square] or a piece from this other sandwich [pointing to the second square] or a piece from the third sandwich [pointing to the third square], which piece would you choose? Would they be the same?

I don't want you to tell me your answer now. Think about it as you work and come up with a way to explain to all of us how you know.

As students start on the problem, the teacher circulates around the room to observe the students at work.

The teacher watches as Paige picks up her scissors and cuts off a rectangular fourth.

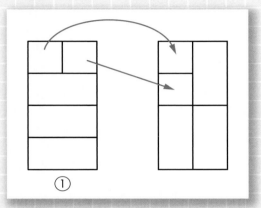

She cuts it in half and places the two parts onto another paper to show a perfect fit over a square fourth.

It takes longer for Paige to see how to do the same with the triangular pieces, but she eventually gets it.

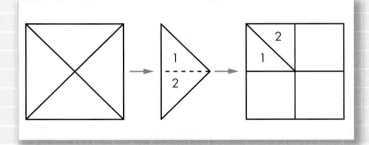

The teacher sees Anita laying out 25 cubes on a fourth in the first square. Then she takes the 25 cubes and lays them out on the second square.

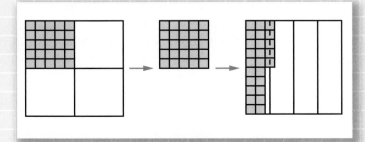

Teacher: How many cubes do you need to cover that rectangular piece?

Anita: [pointing to the five cubes on the right] I need to cut these five cubes and put the pieces down here so you can see that it's the same, 25.

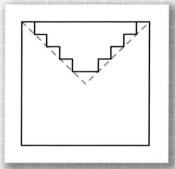

It's harder for Anita to see how the 25 cubes can fit on the triangular piece, so she cuts squares about the size of a cube face, cuts some in half diagonally, and glues them on.

Anita knows that she has covered the triangle with 25 squares. However, because her cutting isn't as precise as this drawing, there are gaps and overlaps, and because it's hard to see that there are 25 squares (20 whole squares and 10 half squares), her demonstration is less convincing to her classmates.

When the teacher asks Jeffrey what he thinks, he simply places one whole square on top of the other.

Teacher: So you're showing that because the squares are the same size, the fourths must be the same size?

Jeffrey: [vigorously nodding his head] Yes!

When the class gathers to discuss their findings, these three students share how they are convinced that the pieces are equal. After their presentations, the teacher encourages the class to continue thinking about how these different shapes can be equal.

Teacher: But we have three different shapes. How can the pieces be equal?

Juanita: Maybe because this (rectangular) piece is the tallest, but it's skinnier than the square and the triangle. The tall pieces are skinnier and the short pieces are fatter.

Estaban: It's how you cut it. If you cut the triangle pieces, they fit on the square.

Teacher: This is a difficult idea, and you have good ways of thinking about it.

Jacy: This proves that it doesn't have to look the same to be the same.

Many second graders do have the resources to take on such a challenging question as whether differently shaped fourths are actually the same quantity. Paige and Anita illustrate two significant strategies to prove that two regions have equal area.

1. Decomposing one region into parts and rearranging the parts over the other region
2. Showing that the same number of units covers both regions

After students have offered their proofs, the teacher asks how different shapes can be equal, challenging the class to think more about their conclusions and, perhaps, voicing confusion that may be shared by some members of the class. This gives Juanita and Esteban further opportunity to verbalize how these shapes are related and gives their classmates the opportunity to think about what they see.

Jacy summarizes the class's findings by observing that "it doesn't have to look the same to be the same," bringing forward the idea that there are different ways to think about what "same" means.

Talking About Fraction Flags

Students created Fraction Flag posters during Session 2.4, and students gathered to discuss their observations. At first, students observe superficial things, such as the colors used and the number of flags on each poster. After a few moments, they begin to discuss important ideas about fractions.

Teacher: What do you notice when you look at these posters?

Chen: Some have the same colors.

Carolina: The "$\frac{1}{2}$ and $\frac{1}{2}$" have 12 flags.

Holly: The one with "$\frac{1}{3}$ and $\frac{1}{3}$ and $\frac{1}{3}$" has 6 flags.

Nadia: There are 43 flags altogether.

Teacher: What do you notice about the flags in particular?

Paige: On this poster, the flags don't look the same, but they have the same number.

Tia: On these 2 posters ($\frac{1}{3}$ and $\frac{1}{3}$ and $\frac{1}{3}$, $\frac{2}{3}$ and $\frac{1}{3}$) each flag has 3 pieces and the bottom number on each is 3.

Holly: And on each poster, if you add the top numbers of the fractions together it equals the bottom number.

Teacher: Holly has made an observation about all of the posters. Let's look at "$\frac{3}{4}$ and $\frac{1}{4}$." She says to add the numerators, or the top numbers. What do we get?

Students: 4.

Teacher: Did we get the denominator, or bottom number?

Students: Yes.

Teacher: Let's try another one.

Students test Holly's idea and they see that it works on all of the posters.

Teacher: Why do you think it works that way?

Students have a difficult time explaining why, and instead offer other observations.

Carla: The "$\frac{1}{3}$ and $\frac{1}{3}$ and $\frac{1}{3}$" poster is kind of like the "$\frac{2}{3}$ and $\frac{1}{3}$." You just have to put 2 of the thirds together to make $\frac{2}{3}$.

Anita: On "$\frac{1}{3}$ and $\frac{1}{3}$ and $\frac{1}{3}$," the flags are 3 colors. On "$\frac{2}{3}$ and $\frac{1}{3}$," the flags are 2 colors.

Carla: Because 2 of the thirds are the same color.

Teacher: Carla has pointed out the posters that have flags divided into thirds. Which posters have flags divided into fourths?

Students make similar observations about the 3 posters divided into fourths.

Teacher: Let's look at the "$\frac{2}{3}$ and $\frac{1}{3}$" poster. How many colors are there in each flag?

Students: Two.

Teacher: Why isn't this flag on the "$\frac{1}{2}$ and $\frac{1}{2}$" poster?

Yama: Because it doesn't have 2 equal parts.

Carla: It's 3 equal parts, and 2 of them are green.

Teacher: I want to talk about one more thing. Esteban made a flag that didn't have a place on a poster. What do you think about this?

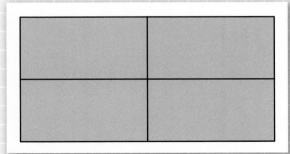

Rochelle: Esteban filled in all of the parts.

Melissa: It's the whole thing so it's one "oneths."

Luis: It's 4 out of 4 parts, so that's 4 fourths.

Henry: Yeah, it's 4 fourths.

Tia: But it's not a fraction.

Teacher: Why isn't it a fraction, Tia?

Tia: Because it's the whole thing. It's not a part.

Henry: That doesn't matter. It's still 4 fourths.

Teacher: Henry is right. It's 4 out of 4 parts, and so 4 fourths are colored blue. And even though it's the whole flag, we still say that 4 fourths is a fraction.

Luis: And 3 thirds will fill the whole flag too.

There are several important points to this discussion. First, some of the students' observations approach the concept of adding fractions. Holly has observed that if you add the numerators (or, as Holly says, the "top numbers") of all of the parts on a poster, you get the denominator. Carla compares the "$\frac{1}{3}$ and $\frac{1}{3}$ and $\frac{1}{3}$" poster and the "$\frac{2}{3}$ and $\frac{1}{3}$" poster. She says, "You just have to put 2 of the thirds together to make $\frac{2}{3}$." These observations lay the foundation for work in later grades, in which students learn more formally how to add fractions.

Second, the teacher uses this discussion as an opportunity to reinforce the idea that fractions involve equal parts. The teacher checks to make sure that students understand the difference between the "$\frac{1}{2}$ and $\frac{1}{2}$" poster and the "$\frac{2}{3}$ and $\frac{1}{3}$" poster, even though they both have flags with only 2 colors. He could also have asked students to compare the "$\frac{2}{4}$ and $\frac{1}{4}$ and $\frac{1}{4}$" poster with the "$\frac{1}{3}$ and $\frac{1}{3}$ and $\frac{1}{3}$" poster.

Finally, the teacher shows a student's flag that doesn't fit on any of the posters, introducing a fraction that represents the whole flag, or $\frac{4}{4}$. Although this idea is not included in the unit, the teacher has recognized an opportunity to bring it to the class, and the class is ready for it. Luis observes that $\frac{3}{3}$ is similar, and that it will also fill the whole flag.

Thirds and Fourths of Sets

Students are about to begin *Student Activity Book* pages 33–34, in which students find thirds and fourths of sets. To introduce the activity to the whole class, the teacher provides a problem in which 3 girls share 12 buttons.

Teacher: Ebony, Linda, and Kira are going to share 12 buttons. Now, close your eyes and picture 12 buttons being shared by the 3 girls. [Pause.] What fraction of the buttons will each girl get? Holly?

Holly: Half.

Teacher: Malcolm?

Malcolm: Half.

Teacher: Alberto?

Alberto: It can't be half. There are 3 girls and 1 would be left out.

Paige: You have to have three thirds. One third, one third, and one third.

Teacher: Why is it thirds and not halves?

Juan: Because there are 3 of them and they all get 1 button.

Teacher: Close your eyes. Sometimes it's better if you can see what's happening. Imagine that there is a jar of buttons. There are 12 buttons in the jar. How many buttons does each girl get? When you open your eyes, discuss it with your partner.

Luis calls the teacher over.

Luis: The answer is 6.

Teacher: OK. So that means Linda gets 6 and Ebony gets 6 and Kira gets 6. If each girl gets 6, what's the total number of buttons? Remember, the girls have just 12 buttons to share.

Luis and Jeffrey get out 12 cubes and distribute them until there are 4 buttons in 3 groups.

The teacher brings the whole class together again.

Teacher: Let's hear what you did. How many buttons does each girl get? What's one third of 12?

Paige: 4.

The class agrees.

Teacher: How did you get 4?

Rochelle: We started with 12 and then we took 4 away from it. Then we counted 4 and took it away and counted 4 more and took it away.

Teacher: How many piles did you make? *(3)* You said that you took a stack of 4 away from the pile. Did you just know that it was going to be 4? How did you know to take away 4?

Rochelle: I knew that 4 plus 4 is 8 and 4 more is 12, so that's 3 stacks of 4.

The teacher records the equations while repeating Rochelle's strategy:

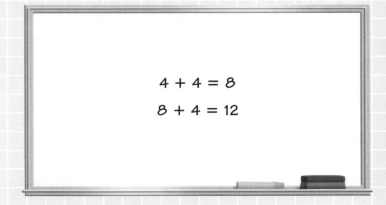

$$4 + 4 = 8$$
$$8 + 4 = 12$$

Next, the teacher points out what Luis and Jeffrey did, prompting them as they explain their error. The teacher records 6, 6, and 6.

Teacher: Did they have equal groups? (*Yes.*) So did they make thirds? (*Yes.*) What's the problem with this?

Jeffrey: It equaled . . . too much.

Teacher: So this was more than 12. What did you do?

Luis: I started to take some away. I ended up with 4.

As students work in pairs on *Student Activity Book* pages 33–34, the teacher has an opportunity to check in with student pairs. Rochelle is working on sharing 24 peanuts among 3 girls and at first thinks that each person gets 3 peanuts, because of thirds. After clarifying what *one third* means, Rochelle and Anita count out 24 cubes.

Teacher: If I had all these peanuts and you took 3 and Anita took 3, would that be fair? (*No.*) Then how should friends share? (*They should get one third.*)

Rochelle recounts the 24 cubes and checks her idea about 3 each. She breaks off 3 groups of 3. After realizing that she has many peanuts left, she pauses to think about it. She then makes 3 trains of 8 cubes.

Teacher: What are you thinking?

Rochelle: 8 plus 8 is 16, and 4 plus 4 is 8, and it ends up on 24. I just know it.

Gregory is working on dividing 24 objects among 4 children. He remembers that he already shared 24 objects among 3 children.

Teacher: Gregory, what did you get when there were 3 girls and each girl got $\frac{1}{3}$ of 24?

Gregory: 8.

Teacher: Do you think you are going to get more or less than 8 for this problem ($\frac{1}{4}$ of 24)?

Gregory: Um, I think more.

Teacher: Could you make a guess of how many each boy is going to get?

Gregory: I think it's going to be 10 or 11.

Teacher: OK, let's see what you get.

Gregory: [Uses cubes and deals them out.] Wait, I got 6. That's less than 8.

Teacher: What do you think is going on?

Gregory: I don't know. I thought it was going to be more than 8 but it wasn't. Oh, wait. I get it! It's because there are *more* people. You have more people, so you get less.

Carolina is working on *Student Activity Book* page 35. The problem involves finding $\frac{1}{4}$ of 7 sandwiches. Carolina can see that each child gets 1 whole sandwich, $\frac{1}{2}$ sandwich, and $\frac{1}{4}$ sandwich.

Carolina: Is this right? (She has written 1, $\frac{1}{2}$, $\frac{1}{4}$.)

Teacher: That's one way to write it, and you can leave it that way if you want to. But what do you know about $\frac{1}{2}$ and $\frac{1}{4}$ that will help you record just one fraction?

Carolina: I don't know.

The teacher draws a picture of a sandwich cut into fourths.

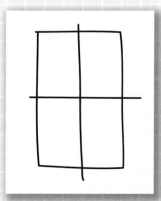

Teacher: Show me half of this sandwich.

Carolina colors in half of the rectangle.

Teacher: So one of the boys got that half sandwich, and he also got another fourth. Show me the fourth.

After Carolina colors in another fourth, her picture looks like this.

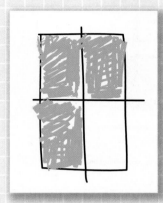

Teacher: Now you have a sandwich with $\frac{1}{2}$ and $\frac{1}{4}$ shaded in. What fraction of the sandwich is shaded in?

Carolina: Oh, $\frac{3}{4}$.

Carolina records $1\frac{3}{4}$ on her paper.

The *Student Activity Book* pages 33–35 allow students to work at different levels. Some students must think harder in order to work with $\frac{1}{3}$ of a set because their first tendency is to find half. The teacher gives these students an opportunity to work out their ideas. Luis and Jeffrey work with their initial idea that if 3 children share 12 buttons, each gets 6. By counting out 6 cubes for each girl, Luis and Jeffrey realize that they have given each girl too many buttons. When the whole class comes back together to discuss the problem, the teacher asks Luis and Jeffrey to explain their error and how they resolved it. This provides the two boys with the opportunity to further solidify their thinking and also helps other students who may be somewhat unsure about the difference between $\frac{1}{2}$ of a set and $\frac{1}{3}$ of a set.

On the other hand, Gregory is encouraged to think about comparing fractions. The teacher asks Gregory, who remembers that $\frac{1}{3}$ of 24 is 8, whether $\frac{1}{4}$ of 24 will be more or less than 8. At first, Gregory makes a common error by thinking that $\frac{1}{4}$ will be more than $\frac{1}{3}$. However, Gregory works out $\frac{1}{4}$ of 24 and sees that the answer is 6. He realizes why it works this way: "You have more people, so you get less."

Carolina, who is quite clear about finding thirds and fourths of sets, goes to *Student Activity Book* page 35 to work on mixed numbers. When her answer to a problem is 1 sandwich, $\frac{1}{2}$ sandwich, and $\frac{1}{4}$ sandwich, the teacher challenges her to use just one fraction to represent the amount. After the teacher helps her draw a picture of the sandwich, Carolina sees that her answer can also be written as $1\frac{3}{4}$.

Student Math Handbook

The *Student Math Handbook* pages related to this unit are pictured on the following pages. This book is designed to be used flexibly: as a resource for students doing classwork, as a book students can take home for reference while doing homework and playing math games with their families, and as a reference for families to better understand the work their children are doing in class.

When students take the *Student Math Handbook* home, they and their families can discuss these pages together to reinforce or enhance students' understanding of the mathematical concepts and games in this unit.

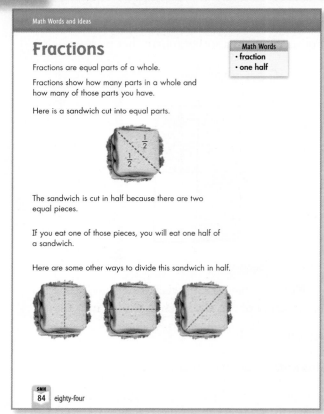

Fractions

Math Words
• fraction
• one half

Fractions are equal parts of a whole.

Fractions show how many parts in a whole and how many of those parts you have.

Here is a sandwich cut into equal parts.

$\frac{1}{2}$
$\frac{1}{2}$

The sandwich is cut in half because there are two equal pieces.

If you eat one of those pieces, you will eat one half of a sandwich.

Here are some other ways to divide this sandwich in half.

SMH
84 eighty-four

◄ Math Words and Ideas, p. 84

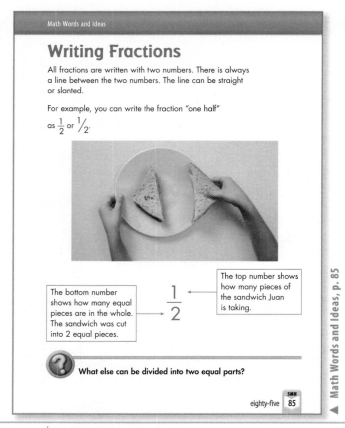

Writing Fractions

All fractions are written with two numbers. There is always a line between the two numbers. The line can be straight or slanted.

For example, you can write the fraction "one half"

as $\frac{1}{2}$ or $^1/_2$.

The bottom number shows how many equal pieces are in the whole. The sandwich was cut into 2 equal pieces.

$\frac{1}{2}$

The top number shows how many pieces of the sandwich Juan is taking.

What else can be divided into two equal parts?

eighty-five SMH 85

◄ Math Words and Ideas, p. 85

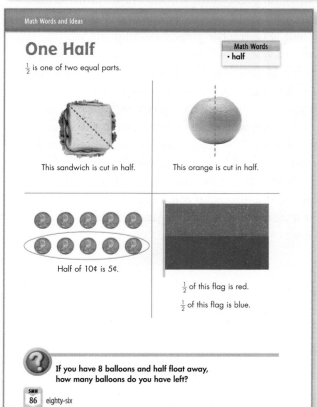

One Half

Math Words
• half

$\frac{1}{2}$ is one of two equal parts.

This sandwich is cut in half.

This orange is cut in half.

Half of 10¢ is 5¢.

$\frac{1}{2}$ of this flag is red.
$\frac{1}{2}$ of this flag is blue.

If you have 8 balloons and half float away, how many balloons do you have left?

SMH 86 eighty-six

◄ Math Words and Ideas, p. 86

One Fourth

$\frac{1}{4}$ is one of four equal parts.

> **Math Words**
> • fourth

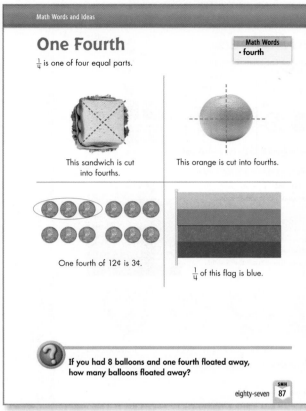

This sandwich is cut into fourths.

This orange is cut into fourths.

One fourth of 12¢ is 3¢.

$\frac{1}{4}$ of this flag is blue.

? If you had 8 balloons and one fourth floated away, how many balloons floated away?

Two Fourths

$\frac{2}{4}$ is two of four equal parts. Two fourths is the same amount as one half ($\frac{1}{2}$).

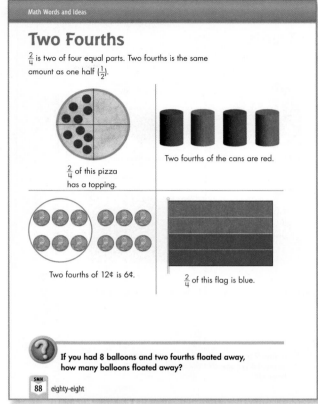

$\frac{2}{4}$ of this pizza has a topping.

Two fourths of the cans are red.

Two fourths of 12¢ is 6¢.

$\frac{2}{4}$ of this flag is blue.

? If you had 8 balloons and two fourths floated away, how many balloons floated away?

Three Fourths

$\frac{3}{4}$ is three of four equal parts.

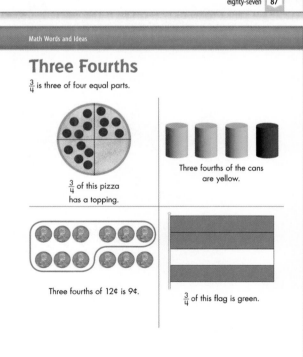

$\frac{3}{4}$ of this pizza has a topping.

Three fourths of the cans are yellow.

Three fourths of 12¢ is 9¢.

$\frac{3}{4}$ of this flag is green.

? If you had 16 balloons and three fourths floated away, how many balloons floated away?

One Third

$\frac{1}{3}$ is one of three equal parts.

> **Math Words**
> • third

One third of this pizza has a topping.

$\frac{1}{3}$ of this cup is filled with juice.

$\frac{1}{3}$ of the balloons are orange.

One third of this flag is red.
One third is white.
One third is blue.

? How many is $\frac{1}{3}$ of nine pennies?

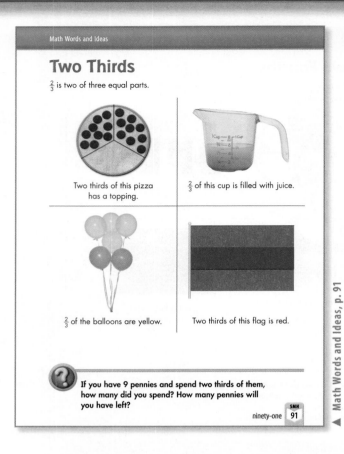

Math Words and Ideas

Two Thirds

$\frac{2}{3}$ is two of three equal parts.

Two thirds of this pizza has a topping.

$\frac{2}{3}$ of this cup is filled with juice.

$\frac{2}{3}$ of the balloons are yellow.

Two thirds of this flag is red.

? If you have 9 pennies and spend two thirds of them, how many did you spend? How many pennies will you have left?

ninety-one **SMH 91**

▲ Math Words and Ideas, p. 91

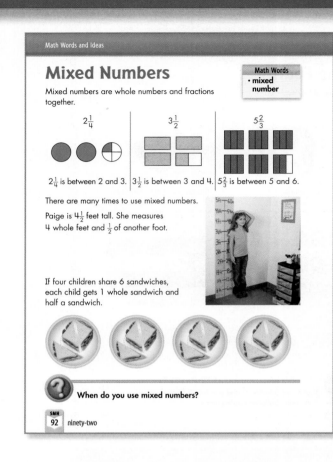

Math Words and Ideas

Mixed Numbers

Math Words
• mixed number

Mixed numbers are whole numbers and fractions together.

$2\frac{1}{4}$

$3\frac{1}{2}$

$5\frac{2}{3}$

$2\frac{1}{4}$ is between 2 and 3. | $3\frac{1}{2}$ is between 3 and 4. | $5\frac{2}{3}$ is between 5 and 6.

There are many times to use mixed numbers.

Paige is $4\frac{1}{2}$ feet tall. She measures 4 whole feet and $\frac{1}{2}$ of another foot.

If four children share 6 sandwiches, each child gets 1 whole sandwich and half a sandwich.

? When do you use mixed numbers?

SMH 92 ninety-two

▲ Math Words and Ideas, p. 92

Index